MAGAZINE

Published by Pedigree in association with **Saga Magazine**.
Pedigree Books Limited, Beech House, Walnut Gardens, Exeter, Devon EX4 4DH.
www.pedigreebooks.com
email: books@pedigreegroup.co.uk
Pedigree trademark, email and website addresses are the sole and exclusive properties of
Pedigree Group Limited, used under licence in this publication.

Saga Magazine – the UK's bestselling monthly magazine.
Available by subscription only: call 0800 056 1057 or visit www.saga.co.uk/magazine-subscriptions
Saga Magazine Enbrook Park, Folkestone, Kent CT20 3SE
Tel: 01303 771523

Yearbook compiled and produced by **Sharon Amos**
Designed by Saga Magazine Art Editor **Kevin Bennett**

Saga Magazine
Editor **Katy Bravery** Art Director **Paul Hayes-Watkins** Designer **Gary Hyde**
Picture Editor **Sue Strange** Picture Researcher **Marianne Scholtz**
Subscriptions Manager **Danielle Chivers**

With thanks to...
Lynne Truss for the Grammar Challenge, ***David Allsop** for ghosting Badger's dog blog, **Ros Badger** for craft projects,
Lesley Bellew, **Amanda Holder** and **David Allsop** for travel features, **David Chapman** for wildlife images and notes,
Piers Fletcher for unexpected anniversaries, **Gary Hyde** for watercolour maps, **Guy Pierce** for the quizzes,
Andy Stevens for techie tips, **James Trollope** for hidden treasures, **Dixe Wills** for island stories...
and all the **Saga Magazine readers** who sent in jokes, pets and beautiful photographs.

All telephone numbers, website details, dates and prices correct at the time of going to press.
Some advance dates may change: always check with the venue before planning a day out.
© 2013 Saga Publishing.

'No idea what to expect inside these pages? Be prepared for a surprise'

If you like recipes and puzzles, witty writing and crafts, gardening and nature, travel and collecting, then you'll love this – our very first Saga Magazine Yearbook. It's been great fun pulling this all together and thinking of things to amuse, enthuse and inform you all the way through 2014.

If you're not a reader of Saga Magazine – incidentally, it's Britain's bestselling monthly magazine – then welcome to your first taste of it. Be prepared to be surprised! This Yearbook is a reflection of the wide-ranging, useful and eclectic features we run in every issue, with all manner of exclusive extras thrown in because, well – why not?

So here you'll find money advice (every month the legendary Paul Lewis writes in our magazine) mingled with jokes sent in by readers. The ones we could print, anyway. There are cartoons alongside an exclusive Grammar Challenge from the magazine's columnist Lynne Truss; inspirational travel ideas; photography from our talented readers; timely health and beauty advice; some gorgeous craft projects – and the world's first column written entirely* by a dog.

May our Yearbook bring you enjoyment every week of 2014!

Katy Bravery
EDITOR, SAGA MAGAZINE

WIN
One of ten free annual subscriptions to Saga Magazine – see p188

DEEP MIDWINTER
**Fields near Stourbridge,
West Midlands**
Photographed by Saga Magazine
reader Trevor Mansell

JANUARY
2014

JANUARY

1
Wednesday
New Year's Day, UK Bank Holiday

2
Thursday
Bank Holiday, Scotland

3
Friday

4
Saturday

5
Sunday

6
Monday

7
Tuesday

8
Wednesday

9
Thursday

10
Friday

11
Saturday

12
Sunday

13
Monday

14
Tuesday

15
Wednesday

16
Thursday

17
Friday

18
Saturday

Saga Magazine has everything you need to fill your days

Diary looking a bit empty this month? Pick up your copy of Saga and turn to the Out There pages. Every month we give you details of events all over the country, from music festivals to literary get-togethers, celebratory anniversaries and days out. We review the latest films and give you the lowdown on what everyone's talking about – from plays, musicals and dance, to unmissable exhibitions. And you can find even more online at **www.saga.co.uk/magazine**. To subscribe call 0800 056 1057 or go to **www.saga.co.uk/magazine-subscriptions**

19
Sunday

20
Monday

21
Tuesday

22
Wednesday

23
Thursday

24
Friday

25
Saturday
Burns' Night

26
Sunday

27
Monday

28
Tuesday

29
Wedesday

30
Thursday

31
Friday

DECADE BUSTERS

JANUARY BIRTHDAYS

TURNING 70
Nick Mason *Pink Floyd musician (right))*
TURNING 60
Trudie Styler *film producer*
TURNING 50
Jane Horrocks *actress*
Anna Ryder Richardson *TV presenter*

REX

RECIPE OF THE WEEK
Chicken Nasi Goreng with Basmati Rice & Spring Greens
Serves 4

Prepare 10 mins **Cook** 15 mins
1–2 tbsp sunflower oil
2 free-range eggs, beaten
1 red pepper, deseeded and thinly sliced
200g pack Waitrose Baby Leaf Greens, shredded
2 red chillies, deseeded and thinly sliced
1 bunch salad onions, sliced
2 x 250g packs Tilda Steamed Basmati Rice
*200g (7oz) Waitrose British Roast Chicken Sweet Chilli Mini
  Fillets, shredded or thinly sliced*
2 tbsp soy sauce
2 tbsp Lingham's Ginger Garlic Chilli Sauce
6cm (2in) piece cucumber, halved, seeded and sliced
*60g pack Waitrose Indonesian Style Vegetable Crackers,
  to serve*

1. Heat a splash of the oil in a large non-stick frying pan
or wok and, once hot, pour in the beaten eggs and
cook for a couple of minutes on each side to make a large,
thin omelette. Slide the omelette on to a large plate, roll
it up and cut into thin ribbons.
2. Add the rest of the oil to the pan and cook the pepper
for 2 minutes. Add the greens and cook for a further
3 minutes on the highest heat so any water released by
the greens evaporates.
3. Stir in half the chillies, the salad onions, rice and chicken
and continue to cook for a further 5 minutes until piping hot.
4. Stir in the soy sauce and chilli sauce and divide between
bowls. Arrange the cucumber, omelette ribbons and
remaining chillies on top and serve with the crackers.
*Recipe and photograph from Waitrose. More than 5,000
recipes can be found at www.waitrose.com/recipes*

THIS WEEK'S TOP TIP
Got a clump of **rhubarb** tucked away in
a corner of the veg plot?

GARDENING

For a crop of early pale pink
stems – the sort sold at
a premium in supermarkets
– start now. Get a carrier
bag or two of straw and
pack it round the crown of
the plant, then cover the
whole lot with an upturned
bucket to keep out the
light. The stems will be
ready to harvest two or
three weeks earlier than
normal – which can be
from March onwards for
the earliest varieties.
   For an even earlier crop,
lift roots in December
and leave them exposed in
the garden for a couple
of weeks. Then pot them
up and cover with black
plastic to exclude the light.
   Bring it into the
greenhouse or garage
and water sparingly. In five
weeks you can pull the
stems ready to eat. Discard
the plant afterwards as
this method of forcing
weakens it severely.

ALL THINGS BRIGHT AND BEAUTIFUL
Waxwing
Waxwings are winter visitors from Scandinavia. They eat
berries, venturing into gardens to feast on rosehips
and cotoneasters, and even to city centres where streets
and car parks have been planted with berry-bearing
trees and shrubs. Their name comes from the curious red
tips to some of the wing feathers, which look
as though they've been dipped in sealing wax.

DON'T QUOTE ME, BUT...
'Looking 50 is great – if you're 60'
Joan Rivers

Toying with a fortune?

Vintage toys don't have to be that old to be worth more than their original retail price. Here is our guide to toys you can't buy with pocket money...

Toys given as **Christmas presents** are often exiled to the attic by January. And if they've been gathering dust for a decade or more, they may also have been gaining value. A child's reject could be a collector's dream, especially if it's in near-mint condition – be it a doll, model car or Meccano set.

For boys, Frank Hornby (1863-1936) was the king of the toy makers, starting with Meccano in 1899 and going on to produce Hornby trains and Dinky cars. He began by making toys at home for his sons, developing his passion into a worldwide business. Most boys loved his products so they are normally bashed around a bit, but even in average condition, they can command healthy prices. An original box almost doubles the value, with some 1930s Dinky toys achieving amazing prices. In 2008 a Dinky Truck advertising a London bicycle shop made nearly £20,000 and another collector paid £35,000 for a boxed set of six vans. Top 1950s sets make hundreds rather than thousands, while vehicles in average condition may still beat their original retail price.

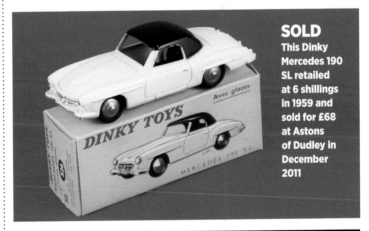

SOLD
This Dinky Mercedes 190 SL retailed at 6 shillings in 1959 and sold for £68 at Astons of Dudley in December 2011

RECIPE OF THE WEEK
Roast Rump of Beef Studded with Garlic & Thyme
Serves 6

Prepare 15 mins + 2 hours marinating **Cook** 40 mins
4 cloves garlic, chopped
½ pack Waitrose Cooks' Ingredients Thyme
2 shallots, sliced
3 tbsp olive oil
850g (1lb 14oz) British beef top rump roast
2 x 350g packs Waitrose Sliced Butternut Squash
500g tub Waitrose Beef Gravy, to serve

1. Preheat the oven to 200C/400F/gas 6. Mix together the garlic, thyme, sliced shallots, olive oil and seasoning in a shallow dish. Add the beef, turning to coat in the marinade, cover and refrigerate for 1½–2 hours, turning a couple of times. Remove from the marinade. Add the squash to the leftover marinade and toss to coat.
2. Heat a heavy-duty roasting tin on the hob over a high heat and brown the beef on all sides, then transfer the tin to the oven and calculate the cooking time: 20 minutes per 500g (1lb) for rare, 25 minutes for medium and 30 minutes for well done. Cook for the calculated time, adding the butternut squash to the tin for the last 40 minutes, and turn once during cooking.
3. Remove the beef from the oven and transfer to a warm platter. Serve with the roasted butternut squash wedges and the heated gravy.
Recipe and photograph from Waitrose. More than 5,000 recipes can be found at www.waitrose.com/recipes

THIS WEEK'S TOP TIP
Running on empty

HEALTH
A bowl of porridge may be just the thing before you venture out for that early morning walk. But if you're trying to lose Christmas pounds, it could be better to delay it. A study from the University of Glasgow revealed that exercising on an empty stomach burned off more body fat and carbohydrates – and helped to lower levels of artery-clogging blood fats – than exercising after eating.

ALL THINGS BRIGHT AND BEAUTIFUL
Holm oak
This evergreen oak is a welcome sight in winter when so many trees are leafless. A sunny day and a grove of holm oaks can fool you into thinking that spring is here. Introduced in the 1500s from the Mediterranean, it's more common in the warmer south of the country, especially on the coast. The name holm oak means holly oak, as the young leaves are spiky, like holly.

DON'T QUOTE ME, BUT...
'If I knew I was going to live this long, I'd have taken better care of myself'
Mickey Mantle

'I SEE FOOD, I EAT IT. HOW AM I SUPPOSED TO KNOW IT'S NOT FOR ME?'

Introducing Badger. You'll be reading her dog's eye view of life every month

**JANUARY
DRINK OF THE MONTH**

BELLINI

Start the New Year in style with this sweet fizz from the famous Harry's Bar in Venice

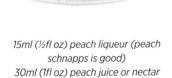

15ml (½fl oz) peach liqueur (peach schnapps is good)
30ml (1fl oz) peach juice or nectar
Chilled prosecco or sparkling wine

Pour the peach liqueur and peach juice into a chilled champagne flute. Slowly top up with prosecco or – champagne if you're flush.

My name is Badger and I am the leader of my pack. I live in a village just down the road from the farm where I was born. When some humans came to look at me and my gormless brothers when we were puppies, the farmer said: 'Take the girl, she's the only one with a brain.'

They looked anxious, but seemed harmless enough in a confused DFL* sort of way and I thought, 'I can work with these two'. So I made their minds up for them by putting on my most lovable expression and licking their ears. It never fails.

I quickly picked up their language. Most of it is in the form of daft 'questions' as in: 'Isn't she just the naughtiest little woofer in the whole wide world?' Ugh. This can mean anything, but most of the time it means that I've probably done something wrong in their eyes, like eat a pork chop that has been left on a table. What do they think I'm going to do? I'm a dog. I see food, I eat it. How am I supposed to know it's not for me? Most of the time I do pretty much what I like, such as chewing my way

through a rattan chair or a dog basket *(see May's blog)*. Sometimes, I let them get their own way, like at the 'New Year' when they drink a lot of 'wine' with their friends and make me join in a celebration called the hokey-cokey round the kitchen table. As you can guess, this is unimaginably humiliating for a dog – especially for a proud Alpha female like me. I don't do dancing. I leave that to fluffy show-offs on *Britain's Got Talent*.

But it's nowhere near as bad as having to wear a red and white fur Santa scarf on Boxing Day in front of 50 baying foxhounds in the village square.

Last time, however, I figured out a good way of putting a stop to this nonsense. It involved a very public need for a 'poo' bag in front of lots of people, including the vicar, and I could see that the female DFL* wasn't happy.

'Your dog,' she said, handing an empty bag to the so-called 'master', and then marching smartly into the pub. I don't think they'll be taking me next year.

*Down From London

RECIPE OF THE WEEK
Spicy Spinach & Kidney Bean Patties
Serves 4

Prepare 20 mins **Cook** 15 mins
1 tbsp groundnut oil
1 green chilli, seeded and chopped
350g (12oz) frozen essential Waitrose Chopped Spinach
¼ tsp grated nutmeg
¼ tsp cayenne pepper
¼ tsp ground cinnamon
400g can essential Waitrose Red Kidney Beans, drained
1 medium egg, beaten
½ x 130g carton Waitrose Cooks' Ingredients Lemon & Pepper Crust
350g carton Waitrose Organic Tomato & Roasted Garlic Sauce, warmed, to serve

1. Heat one teaspoon of the oil in a small frying pan and add the chilli. Cook for a minute then add the frozen spinach; cover and cook for 4–5 minutes until soft. Season and stir in the nutmeg, cayenne pepper and cinnamon. Simmer until all the liquid evaporates. Allow to cool slightly.
2. Mash the kidney beans in a bowl with a fork or potato masher and stir in the spinach mixture. Shape into 16 patties using floured hands as the mixture is quite soft. Dip them in the egg then the lemon and pepper crust to coat completely. Chill until needed.
3. Heat the remaining oil in a non-stick frying pan and fry the patties on both sides for 5–6 minutes until piping hot and golden. This may need to be done in batches. Drain on kitchen paper and serve with the heated tomato and roasted garlic sauce.
Recipe and photograph from Waitrose. More than 5,000 recipes can be found at www.waitrose.com/recipes

THIS WEEK'S TOP TIP
Don't hang on to vouchers

MONEY
Spend Christmas gift vouchers promptly
– if a retailer goes out of business you may have a hard time getting any money back. If you have a gift voucher, you'll be deemed to be an 'unsecured creditor' with no rights to receiving either goods to the value of the voucher or money in lieu. So make sure you exchange them as soon as possible – and also take into account the risks involved when buying them to give as presents.

ALL THINGS BRIGHT AND BEAUTIFUL
Gorse
Country lore has it that 'when gorse is out of blossom, kissing is out of fashion', simply because you can nearly always find a handful of bright yellow flowers somewhere on a bush. When a bush is in full flower and the sun is shining, the surrounding air can smell strongly of coconut – but don't be tempted to sniff too closely, as the plant is covered in fierce spines. The dense bushes are a valuable wildlife habitat, providing shelter to small birds in winter and safe nesting sites inaccessible to predators for warblers and yellowhammers.

DON'T QUOTE ME, BUT...
'A belief of mine: that everyone else my age is an adult, whereas I am merely in disguise'
Margaret Atwood

TINY ISLANDS
AT LAND'S END

You can walk across to St Michael's Mount at low tide

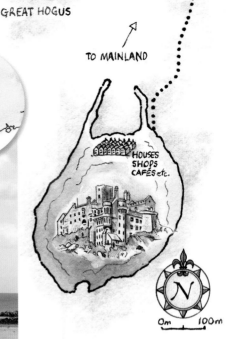

GREAT HOGUS

TO MAINLAND

HOUSES
SHOPS
CAFÉS etc.

N

0m   100m

ST MICHAEL'S MOUNT
Nr Marazion, Cornwall
Size: 7 acres
Population: 33

Fable has it that Land's End was joined to the Isles of Scilly by a land called Lyonesse until 1099. In this year a great flood inundated the area – killing all the inhabitants bar one man (who saved himself by riding the waves on a white charger) – and created the coastline we have today. The flood waters also burst inland around St Michael's Mount, leaving it stranded a quarter of a mile from the newly formed Mount's Bay. In reality, the tidal island is likely to have held that status for about 5,000 years, though one can see why it would be more fun to ascribe its creation to a single cataclysmic event.

Amble across the well-maintained causeway today and you'll find more of interest on its meagre seven acres than in many a large town on the mainland. There's a landward-facing harbour and terraces of neat houses behind it, in which the majority of the population live; a 14th-century priory church; a cemetery; a castle, complete with mummified cat, Samurai warrior and a magnificent Bronze Age hoard discovered on the island in 2009; sub-tropical gardens featuring plants from the Canary Islands, Mexico and South Africa, among others; three pillboxes left over from World War II; a curious collection of bronze casts of the footprints of royal visitors,

including Queen Victoria, Edward VII, Prince Charles and the Duchess of Cornwall; and an underground tram that ferries freight up to the castle from the harbour. This unlikely miniature railway, built more than 100 years ago, still serves the St Aubyn family today, although sadly the public aren't allowed to interact with it.

However, this is an island that is so much more than the collection of things that have accumulated on it over the centuries. To visit St Michael's Mount is to view something of the quiddity of Albion: the singular and often bizarre beliefs, events and people that have helped make England what it is. What's all the more remarkable is that St Michael's Mount isn't even in England. As anyone born in Cornwall will be quick to tell you, this is a country unto itself – if you want to see England, you'll have to go east of the Tamar river.

HOW TO GET THERE
From Penzance railway station there's a 2.5-mile cycle/footpath around Mount's Bay that takes you practically all the way to the head of the causeway. Alternatively, take the 2/2A bus to Marazion. The island is accessible for roughly four hours at each low tide. When the tide is in, you can catch one of the little ferries that serve the island from 9am to 5pm when the causeway is closed.

THIS WEEK'S TOP TIP
Feeling somewhat jaded but need to look your best?

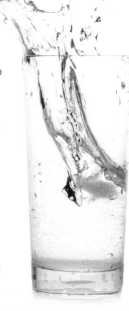

BEAUTY
Only had a few hours' sleep but need to create a good impression? Try these cheats to looking good. First, make sure your body is properly hydrated by drinking plenty of water. Dehydration shows in your skin. Then give your face a healthy glow by exfoliating to slough off dead cells and stimulate new cell growth. Finish off with a tinted moisturiser to boost that healthy glow, and you will feel ready to face the world.

RECIPE OF THE WEEK
Vanilla & Lemon Pudding
Serves 6

Prepare 15 mins **Cook** 45 mins
175g (6oz) golden caster sugar
Finely grated zest and juice of 2 large lemons
50g (2oz) essential Waitrose Dairy Butter, softened,
*   plus extra for greasing*
3 medium Columbian Blacktail free-range eggs, separated
1 tsp Nielsen-Massey vanilla extract
50g (2oz) plain flour
250ml (9fl oz) whole milk
Icing sugar, for dusting
Cream or ice cream, to serve

1. Heat the oven to 180C/350F/gas 4. Place the sugar, lemon zest and juice, butter, egg yolks, vanilla extract and flour in a large bowl. Using an electric hand whisk, beat the mixture until smooth. Whisk in the milk.
2. In a separate bowl, using clean beaters, whisk the egg whites until firm. Fold the egg whites into the batter mixture, then pour into a buttered ovenproof dish.
3. Sit the dish in a roasting tin and pour in boiling water so it comes halfway up the sides of the dish. Bake for 40–45 minutes until the sponge top is dark and just set and a lemon custard has formed beneath. Dust lightly with icing sugar and serve warm with cream or ice cream.
Recipe and photograph from Waitrose. More than 5,000 recipes can be found at www.waitrose.com/recipes

ALL THINGS BRIGHT AND BEAUTIFUL
Blackcap
Back in the Seventies, blackcaps visited our gardens and woodlands in summer, rearing their chicks before heading off to Spain and North Africa. Now there's evidence that many of them are opting to stay here for the winter – perhaps due to our unfailing habit of feeding garden birds. If you're interested in monitoring their numbers – and those of other species – join in the RSPB's Big Garden Birdwatch this month (www.rspb.org/birdwatch/).

DON'T QUOTE ME, BUT...
'Never regret. If it's good, it's wonderful. If it's bad, it's experience'
Victoria Holt

UNEXPECTED ANNIVERSARIES
JUST IMAGINE

January 2014 is the 113th anniversary of:
the death of Queen Victoria

During 2013, the rules governing the succession to the throne were changed so that Prince William's oldest child would be first in line to succeed him as monarch, regardless of gender. It's hard to object to that. But if this rule had been in place in 1901, Queen Victoria would have been succeeded by her oldest daughter, Vicky, instead of Edward VII. Vicky died soon after her mother, and would have been succeeded by her own son, with the consequence that, when the First World War broke out, the King of Great Britain (and its Empire) would have been... the Kaiser.

PET OF THE MONTH
Snow dog

Name: Boot
Owner's name: Alfie Durrant
Best habit: Always being cheerful
Worst habit: Crazy barking fits at 3am
Likes: Curling up with the soft toy
dog he had as a puppy
Dislikes: Anyone coming near said
soft toy dog
Personality: Adoring, fun, playful
Naughtiest moment: Pooing all over
his master's homework book
Most human trait: Hates being
left alone

TOP TECHIE TIP
Top of the forum

Out in the wonderful world of the web there are discussion forums covering every topic under the sun. If you're not sure of the website address for a forum that interests you, click about on the search engine omgili.com, which is set up for that purpose. You'll usually have to register to join a forum: this is par for the course and not too long-winded. Once you join, make sure you introduce yourself (best practice is under a nickname).

An online forum that's well-run, sensible and which covers engaging subjects can be a great outlet for a spot of coffee-break banter.

JOKE OF THE MONTH
I called the swine flu advice line and all I got was crackling.

sent in by Judith Cleverly

HOW TO MAKE A HOT-WATER BOTTLE COVER

This cosy hot-water bottle cover is a clever way to make use of an old jersey. It's an improvement on shop-bought versions, as it opens at the bottom so it won't get damaged by having to be stretched over the stopper

WHAT YOU'LL NEED
Large piece of paper
Old jersey, preferably in soft cashmere or felted wool, to avoid the pieces unravelling as you work
Cotton thread to match jersey colour

WHAT TO DO
1. Draw around your hot-water bottle, adding 1.5cm (½in) all around for a seam allowance. Then make two paper pattern pieces as follows:

Piece A: this must be at least 5cm (2in) longer than piece B.

Piece B needs to be approximately 1cm (½in) shorter than the hot-water bottle. Cutting the pattern pieces to these dimensions allows for the longer piece A to overlap both the base of the bottle and also the shorter piece B, creating the envelope opening.
2. Cut out the two pattern pieces from your jersey, being sure to place the bottom edge of each pattern piece along the natural edge of the knitting.
3. Fold up the bottom 5cm (2in) of piece A, right side to right side, and pin or tack in place at the edges. Then, with right sides facing, place pieces A and B together, matching up the tops. At this stage, piece B should now be about 1cm (½in) shorter than piece A.
4. Sew around the cover using a small zigzag stitch on a sewing machine, or use back stitch if sewing by hand. Do not sew along the folded edge.
5. Turn right sides out and bring the 5cm (2in) fold to the front to create the envelope edge that secures your hot-water bottle in place.

TOP TIP This cover looks and feels good made out of pieces cut from an old blanket, too.

USE IT OR LOSE IT
BRAIN EXERCISE
Give your grey matter a work-out

SUDOKU
The game of logic. Place each of the digits 1 to 9 in each row, column and 3x3 box. There is only one solution.

					7		3	
6	2			4		9		
				5				7
	7			9	1	8		
	9	1				5	2	
		6	8	5			7	
7			2					
	3		8				9	4
	4		5					

GRAMMAR CHALLENGE
The Lynne Truss test Can you spot the errors in grammar, punctuation and spelling? See below for the correct version.

at this time of the year most of the color has drained from our gardens but i was surprised to visit one and see lots of alium heads which often disintigrate by the autumn in tip top order the secret remove them while there perfect dry them indoors and return them to the garden for special occasions lets say you are expecting guests on a frosty day i tried the same with the thistle like heads of acanthers but i had not been warned about the exploding seeds it was like the gunfight at the ok coral as they ricoshayed of the walls

At this time of the year, most of the colour has drained from our gardens, but I was surprised to visit one and see lots of allium heads, which often disintegrate by the autumn, in tip-top order. The secret? Remove them while they're perfect, dry them indoors, and return them to the garden for a special occasion (let's say you are expecting guests on a frosty day). I tried the same with the thistle-like heads of acanthus, but I had not been warned about the exploding seeds; it was like the gunfight at the OK Corral as they ricochetted off the walls.

JANUARY'S GENERAL KNOWLEDGE QUIZ
1. The Roman god Janus boasts what distinguishing feature?
A. Two heads, B. Two faces, C. A forked tongue, D. A beard of snakes

2. Which group had a hit with the song *January*, which was No 1 in February 1975?
A. Badfinger, B. Sailor, C. Edison Lighthouse, D. Pilot

3. First published as *The Times* on January 1, 1788, by what name was the newspaper formerly known?
A. *The National Record*, B. *The Daily Universal Register*, C. *The Thunderer*, D. *The London Opinion*

4. Why do the residents of the Gwaun Valley in Pembrokeshire mark the New Year on January 13?
A. To avoid paying council tax, B. They follow the Julian calendar, C. To annoy the English, D. The local pub opens only on that day in January

5. Which country celebrates Coming of Age Day on the second Monday of January?
A. South Korea, B. Canada, C. Japan, D. Finland

6. In January 1697, Thomas Aikenhead was the last man to be executed in Britain for which crime?
A. Blasphemy, B. Necromancy, C, Embezzlement, D. Libel

7. Elvis Presley was the surviving twin at birth on January 8, 1935. What was his brother called?
A. Brenton, B. Jesse, C. Levi, D. Waylon

8. To whom, or what, did Robert Burns address these words? 'Fair fa' your honest, sonsie face…'
A. Flora MacDonald, B. A mouse, C. A haggis, D. Bonnie Prince Charlie

9. Which U2 album featured the song *New Year's Day*?
A. *Boy*, B. *War*, C. *October*, D. *The Unforgettable Fire*

10. The euro came into being on January 1, 1999. What is on the obverse side of a €1 coin?
A. A dove, B. A pair of hands, C. A map of Europe, D. A sunrise

---

ANSWERS

1. B, 2. D,
3. B, 4. B,
5. C, 6. A,
7. B, 8. C,
9. B, 10. C

1	9	7	6	3	5	8	4	2
4	6	2	9	8	7	3	5	1
8	5	3	4	1	2	6	9	7
6	1	7	2	5	8	9	3	4
9	2	5	3	7	4	1	6	8
3	4	8	1	6	9	2	7	5
7	8	9	5	2	6	4	1	3
5	1	6	8	4	3	7	2	9
2	3	4	7	9	1	5	8	6

BARBADOS

Bound by miles of spotless white sandy beaches, this
Caribbean jewel has a fascinating history and a
warm and friendly vibe. It's pretty lively after dark, too

FIVE Q&As

Where is Barbados? It is the most
easterly of the Lesser Antilles, in the
Caribbean, with 700 miles of beaches.

How's the weather? Expect 3,000
hours of sunshine a year. The
dry season is from December to May,
when temperatures average 26C.

Will I see any celebs? Probably,
especially if you stay on the west coast.
Simon Cowell flies in on his private jet,
Oprah Winfrey has stayed at Sandy
Lane, and the Beckhams holiday on
the Platinum Coast. Cilla Black owns
a property, and so does Cliff Richard.

Any bright lights? Plenty! St Lawrence
Gap, with its ocean view, has a friendly,
buzzy vibe. Pisces restaurant on the

waterside offers traditional Bajan
(Barbadian) cuisine, including a huge
seafood menu. Café Sol, the island's
original Mexican restaurant, doubles
as a lively open-air margarita bar
with not one but two happy hours:
5pm-7pm and 10pm-midnight. Cheers!

In the capital, Bridgetown, the
Barbados Crop Over celebration
originally marked the end of the sugar
harvest. It's now a public holiday
when the town pulsates with calypso
rhythms, culminating in The Grand
Kadooment, a street carnival with
a great deal of energetic dancing.

You will see surfers riding 15ft waves and troupes of green monkeys in the trees

What's the history? Barbados is
a coral island, pushed out of the sea
by volcanic activity about a million
years ago. Amerindians from
Venezuela were the first inhabitants:
the Arawak Indians, who were ousted
by the Carib Indians in the 13th
century. The British discovered the
island in 1625 and settled in 1627.
The climate was ideal for growing
sugar cane, giving rise to many
plantations. Thousands of slaves were
brought in from West Africa, and
sugar, with its by-products molasses
and rum, was the source of enormous
wealth for some, and misery for many.

The island gained full independence
from the British Empire in 1966 but
remains part of the Commonwealth.
In 2011, Bridgetown and its garrison
became a UNESCO World Heritage site.

Seahorses
Head to Pebbles Beach at dawn for the magical sight of racehorses going for an early morning swim, a welcome change from pounding the sun-baked turf on the track

BARBADOS
LAT. 13°N
LONG. 59°W

Fun in the sun
At Bottom Bay *(main pic)*, the beach is protected by coral cliffs; rum is the island's drink of choice

FOUR REASONS TO VISIT

Unspoilt beaches Bottom Bay and Foul Bay, both on the southeastern coast, are popular with Bajan locals, although visitors are welcome, too. There are no bars or cafés, so take a picnic. The Atlantic waves are much stronger here than on the western (Caribbean) side of the island.

A rum day out St Nicolas Abbey, in the north of the island, is a colonial stately home built in 1660 and one of only three remaining Jacobean mansions in the western hemisphere.

There is a rum and sugar museum tracing the plantation's history, including records of slaves. The abbey also makes its own rum – a great souvenir to take home – and the park-like gardens feature mahogany and avocado trees and cabbage palms.

Botanist's paradise There are an astounding 700 species of flowering plants on the island's 166 sq miles. Andromeda Botanical Garden, on the east coast, has the largest collection of tropical plants in the Eastern Caribbean, while the Flower Forest, in the Scotland district, offers spectacular views across the hills to Chalky Mount along with ginger lilies, heliconias and bird of paradise plants. Look out for green monkeys capering in the trees at Welchman Hall Gully, a tropical forest near Harrison's Cove in the centre of the island.

Surf's up, dude! The ruggedly beautiful east coast is less touristy than elsewhere. Bathsheba, in the parish of St Joseph, features wide beaches dotted with unusual rock formations. As with Bottom Bay, the shore is pounded by the Atlantic and you can watch surfers ride vertical waves of up to 15ft in the 'Soup Bowl'. Kelly Slater, one of the world's top surfers, rates Bathsheba as his favourite, but surfing here is not recommended for learners.

THREE THINGS TO KNOW
Rum is the national drink and rum punch is the perfect way to enjoy it.

Singer Rihanna was born in Barbados – she moved to the US at 16.

Drive on the left, just as in the UK.

TWO THINGS TO AVOID
The manchineel tree in the rain. If you stand underneath it, raindrops running off the fruit cause blisters.

Swimming on the east coast. The waves are wonderful for jumping in but too dangerous for swimming.

ONE MUST-DO
Bajans love the sport of kings. The Garrison Savannah racetrack is one of the oldest in the Americas. Spectators come from all over the world for The Sandy Lane Barbados Gold Cup on the first Saturday in March. And at Pebbles Beach, each morning at dawn, grooms from the nearby racetrack take the horses down to the sea for an early morning swim. The horses are then washed and groomed while the men sing them calypso songs. Well worth getting up early for.

Does Saga go there?
Yes, find out more about travel to Barbados at saga.co.uk/holidays

FEBRUARY
2014

FEBRUARY

1
Saturday

2
Sunday

3
Monday

4
Tuesday

5
Wednesday
Retrospective Richard Deacon, sculptor
Tate Britain, Millbank, London (to April 27)

6
Thursday

7
Friday

8
Saturday

9
Sunday

10
Monday

11
Tuesday

12
Wednesday

13
Thursday
Retrospective Richard Hamilton, painter
Tate Modern, Bankside, London (to May 26)

14
Friday
Valentine's Day

15
Saturday

16
Sunday

17
Monday

18
Tuesday

Saga Magazine has everything you need to fill your days

Diary looking a bit empty this month? Pick up your copy of Saga and turn to the Out There pages.
Every month we give you details of events all over the country, from music festivals to literary
get-togethers, celebratory anniversaries and days out. We review the latest films and give you the lowdown
on what everyone's talking about – from plays, musicals and dance, to unmissable exhibitions.
And you can find even more online at **www.saga.co.uk/magazine**. To subscribe call 0800 056 1057
or go to **www.saga.co.uk/magazine-subscriptions**

19
Wednesday

20
Thursday

21
Friday

22
Saturday

23
Sunday

24
Monday

25
Tuesday

26
Wednesday

27
Thursday

28
Friday

DECADE BUSTERS

FEBRUARY BIRTHDAYS

TURNING 70
Roger Lloyd Pack *actor*
Bruce Fogle *vet*

TURNING 60
Anthony Head *actor*

TURNING 50
Christopher Eccleston
actor
Lee Evans
comedian and actor
Trinny Woodall
(right) fashion expert

RECIPE OF THE WEEK
Light at Heart Chocolate Tart
Serves 8

Prepare 15 mins **Cook** 25 mins
90g (3½oz) essential Waitrose Porridge Oats
50g (2oz) plain flour
25g (1oz) Tate & Lyle Light at Heart White Sugar
60g (2½oz) unsalted butter, cubed

For the filling:
150g (5oz) Waitrose Cook's Ingredients Dark Chocolate,
* broken into pieces*
60g (2½oz) Tate & Lyle Light at Heart Brown Sugar
50g (2oz) unsalted butter
50g (2oz) plain flour
4 medium Columbian Blacktail free-range eggs, beaten
Waitrose Half-Fat Crème Fraîche, to serve
Berries, to serve

1. Heat the oven to 180C/350F/gas 4. Place the oats, flour,
white sugar and butter in a food processor and whizz
to make crumbs. Add 3-4 tbsp cold water and whizz again
until the mixture starts to stick together.
2. Press it firmly into the base of a 20cm (8in) non-stick,
loose-bottomed tart tin. Sit the tin on a baking sheet
and bake for 10 minutes until just set but still pale.
3. Meanwhile, for the filling, gently heat the chocolate,
brown sugar and butter in a small pan until melted, then
pour into a large bowl and leave to cool for 5 minutes.
Beat in the flour and eggs.
4. Pour the chocolate mixture into the prepared tin and
bake for 15 minutes until just set. Leave to cool in the
tin for a few minutes, then lift out and cool on a wire rack.
Slice and serve with crème fraîche and berries.
Recipe and photograph from Waitrose. More than 5,000
recipes can be found at www.waitrose.com/recipes

THIS WEEK'S TOP TIP
Sow **sweet peas** indoors for a head start

GARDENING
There are a number of
tricks to help sweet pea
seeds germinate. You can
soak them in a saucer of
water overnight, carefully
nick the seed coat with a
sharp knife (at the opposite
end to the seed's 'eye') or
rub the seed coat lightly
with sandpaper – the seed
packet will specify which
method is best.

Sweet pea plants have
long, deep roots: an ideal
way to grow them is to use
cardboard tubes from the
middle of toilet rolls. Cram
these tightly in an ordinary
plastic flower pot and fill
with damp compost. Add
one prepared seed per tube
and push it gently into the
compost with your finger.

Put the pot in a plastic
bag to act as a cloche.
Once the seedlings begin
to grow, take off the plastic
bag. Pinch out the tips
when the seedlings have
four leaves. Once growing
strongly, harden plants off
before planting outdoors,
cardboard tube and all.

ALL THINGS BRIGHT AND BEAUTIFUL
Frogs
In milder spells, this is the month common frogs
get together in ponds all over the country to mate. Since
they tend to return to their birthplace to spawn, a small
garden pond can become a mass of croaking suitors.
Females lay eggs by the thousand and the protective jelly
– the spawn – swells up to protect them. Frogspawn
is tough stuff and can survive freezing temperatures.

DON'T QUOTE ME, BUT...
'She was a handsome woman of 45 and would remain so for many years'
Anita Brookner

Don't write them off

The best old fountain pens have gone up in value, especially those with novelty features or elegant styling. Here is our guide to pens and penmanship

Most of us have abandoned fountain pens for Biros and computers, but let's hope you've kept some mementos of your inky past. Letter writing may have gone out of fashion, but pen collecting is on the increase. Waterman introduced the first fountain pen in 1883 and demand was steady up until 1958 when throwaway ballpoints came on to the European mass market. Besides Waterman, other names to look out for are Parker, Sheaffer, Conway Stewart, Montblanc and Wahl-Eversharp.

Collectors are fascinated by unusual filling mechanisms and nibs, as well as elegant styling. Perhaps the most successful pen was the Parker 51 which, in one poll, was voted the fourth best industrial design of the 20th century. First sold in 1941 and marketed as 'the world's most wanted pen', it stayed in production until 1972. With its hooded gold nib it was said to 'write dry with wet ink'. General MacArthur used one to sign the Japanese surrender in 1945. Good examples today can fetch several hundred pounds. Rarer, decorative pens may fetch thousands.

SOLD

Stan Laurel wrote thousands of autographs during his career. This photo, signed for a relative on Tyneside, fetched £840 at auction at Anderson and Garland in Newcastle, September 2010

REDISCOVERED BOOK

'This is a proper spy story – a rare find nowadays'

Assignment in Brittany
Helen MacInnes
(Titan, £7.99)

Matthew Hearne, British Intelligence agent, returns from a mission in France to find he is to be sent straight back, posing as Bertrand Corlay, a Frenchman to whom he bears an uncanny resemblance. The plan is that he will gather information about the Nazi occupation, but to do this he needs to fool not only the Germans but also the women in Bertrand's life. *Assignment in Brittany* was first published in 1942 and is a proper spy story – a rare find nowadays.

As chosen by the staff of Slightly Foxed bookshop, specialists in unusual titles, old and new; www.foxedbooks.com

'Ah, here's Gavin now. He's insulating the loft...'

RECIPE OF THE WEEK
Savoury Lamb Meatballs
Serves 4

Prepare 20 mins **Cook** 20 mins
400g (14oz) lamb mince
1 red onion, finely chopped
½ x 25g pack fresh flat-leaf parsley, leaves chopped,
*   plus a few whole leaves to garnish*
2 cloves garlic, finely chopped
35g (1½oz) pitted green olives, finely chopped
1 tbsp Patum Peperium The Gentleman's Relish
1 medium free-range egg, beaten
1 tbsp olive oil
350g tub Waitrose Cherry Tomato & Basil Sauce
300g (11oz) essential Waitrose orzo

1. Place the mince in a large bowl and add the red onion, chopped parsley, garlic, olives, Gentleman's Relish and egg. Using your hands, bring everything together until well combined. Roll into 24 walnut-sized balls and chill on a plate for 10 minutes, or longer if you have time.
2. Heat the oil in a large sauté pan over a medium heat. Add the meatballs and fry for 12–14 minutes until browned all over and cooked through. Add the tomato sauce to the pan and gently heat until bubbling and piping hot.
3. Meanwhile, cook the orzo in a pan of boiling water, according to pack instructions, for 7 minutes. Drain well and divide between 4 shallow bowls. Top with the meatballs and tomato sauce and garnish with a few parsley leaves.
Recipe and photograph from Waitrose. More than 5,000 recipes can be found at www.waitrose.com/recipes

THIS WEEK'S TOP TIP
Echinacea can help beat
the common cold

HEALTH
The largest ever study into the effect of the herbal remedy **echinacea** on the common cold has backed up claims that it significantly reduces your chances of catching a cold. Extract of echinacea or purple coneflower, an American wildflower, is a traditional remedy used by Native Americans to treat coughs, colds and sore throats.

The study carried out at the Common Cold Centre at Cardiff University found that taking three doses a day reduced the number of colds that participants caught – and how long the cold lasted – by an average of 26%, compared with those taking a placebo.

ALL THINGS BRIGHT AND BEAUTIFUL
Snowdrops
The old name of Candlemas bells is a clue to their early flowering – the church festival is marked on February 2. Botanists have decided snowdrops are not native wildflowers, but they've become naturalised in churchyards and along hedgerows. They've also sparked a new craze akin to tulip fever, with some of the 20 species and 500 varieties changing hands for hundreds of pounds for just one bulb.

DON'T QUOTE ME, BUT...
'I'm aiming by the time I'm 50 to stop being an adolescent'
Wendy Cope

'LAST YEAR HE GOT ME A SQUEAKY RUBBER CHICKEN'

In which Badger introduces us to Wilf, her boyfriend, and muses on the pointlessness of names

This time of year, I'm not at my cunning best. It's the snow. I can't help myself. It's like the doorbell ringing endlessly, sending me into convulsions of giddy excitement. 'Where's it gone? Where's it gone?' the male DFL repeats irritatingly when he throws a 'snowball'. And when I try to catch the thing it disappears on the end of my nose. GRRRR.

I think I'm supposed to refer to him as the 'master'. But that's never going to happen. More often I use her name for him which is 'BOG'. This is short for 'Bolshy Old Git'. I don't know what this means, but I expect it's a term of affection. He calls her, with equal affection, 'GOB'. I don't think this is short for anything.

Anyway, that's enough about them. Have I mentioned Wilf? I love Wilf.

He's my boyfriend. I'm not sure what kind of dog he is. Neither is he. He has short fat legs, wiry grey hair that sticks out everywhere, and at first sight you might not know which end is which. Actually in Wilf's case, it's not that difficult once you start sniffing. Even humans can quickly work it out. Every February 14, I get a present from him. It's usually a big marrow bone, which is my favourite. Last year he got me a squeaky rubber chicken from Tesco, with not a hint of marrow, or liver pâté or cheese or anything else worth eating. I don't know what he was thinking of. (He won't try that again in a hurry.) This year he got me two marrow bones, which is much more like it.

By the way, did I tell you that GOB has a different nickname for me every month? I don't know what's wrong with the name Badger (to be honest I'd have preferred something like Angelina or Madonna, or something more befitting my status as a village icon), but she likes to call me something different all the time – probably just to annoy me. This month my name is: 'Minkles Munkles'. I have no idea what this means. Neither does anybody else.

Best moment:
Sick on the seagrass in the lounge. Too much marrow bone

**FEBRUARY
DRINK OF THE MONTH**

HOT TODDY

Everyone has a cold in February – ward it off with one of these at bedtime!

*1 tbsp soft brown sugar
4 slices of lemon
3 cinnamon sticks
10 whole cloves
125ml (4fl oz) Scotch whisky*

Put all the ingredients in a heatproof jug with 1 litre (2 pints) boiling water. Stir, leave for a few minutes, then strain. Pour into heatproof glasses. Serves 4.

RECIPE OF THE WEEK
Slow Spiced Pork with Dried Fruit & Walnut
Serves 6–8

Prepare 20 mins **Cook** 2 hours 30 mins

800g (1lb 12oz) Duchy Originals From Waitrose Organic British Pork Diced Leg or any stewing pork leg or shoulder
2 tbsp plain flour, seasoned
3 tbsp sunflower oil
1 large onion, sliced
3 sticks celery, sliced
2 cloves garlic, chopped
1 tsp ground cinnamon
1 tsp ground mace
1 tsp mild curry powder
2 tbsp thyme leaves
100g (4oz) soft dates, chopped
100g (4oz) soft apricots, chopped
Juice of 1 orange
500ml (18fl oz) Louis Jadot 2009/10 Mâcon-Azé white wine
25g (1oz) walnut pieces
Chopped parsley, to serve

1. Preheat the oven to 170C/325F/gas 3. Toss the pork in the seasoned flour to coat. Heat half the oil in a non-stick frying pan and fry the pork on all sides until browned. Remove with a slotted spoon and place in an ovenproof casserole dish.
2. Heat the remaining oil in the frying pan, add the sliced onion, celery and chopped garlic and cook gently for 3-4 minutes until softened.
3. Add the spices and cook for a minute.
4. Add the thyme leaves, dates, apricots, orange juice and wine.
5. Season and bring to the boil.
6. Pour over the pork in the casserole dish and place in the oven for 1½–2 hours until the pork is tender. To serve, dry fry the walnut pieces and scatter the chopped parsley over the top.
Recipe and photograph from Waitrose. More than 5,000 recipes can be found at www.waitrose.com/recipes

THIS WEEK'S TOP TIP
Sharing your tax allowance

MONEY

There are 12 million people of state pension age in Britain but 4.9 million of them don't use all of their personal tax allowance. In cases where only one partner pays tax, they could reduce their tax bill by transferring savings and investments into the name of the partner who pays no tax. But bear in mind that if this partner needed to have their finances assessed for going into long-term care, the transferred savings will be treated as belonging solely to them.

ALL THINGS BRIGHT AND BEAUTIFUL
Chiffchaff
The clue to the chiffchaff's song is in its name. And hearing it is one of the first signs of spring as these small visiting warblers arrive from southern Europe or north Africa, to breed in the UK. Chiffchaffs are unassuming olive brown birds so are quite hard to spot in the dense bushes and undergrowth they frequent, but their song is unmistakable. Listen out for it in parks, woodland and even large gardens.

DON'T QUOTE ME, BUT...
'The person who views the world at 50 the same as they did at 20 has wasted 30 years of their life'
Muhammad Ali

NOVEL SETTING

An elegant island in the Thames with
a literary past

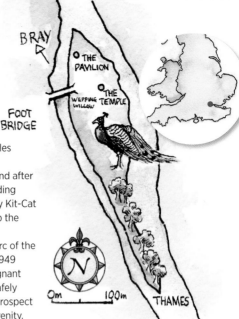

MONKEY ISLAND
River Thames, nr Bray, Berkshire
Size: 4.5 acres
Population: 0

The year 1666 hasn't gone down in the annals as a glorious one in the history of London. However, it's an ill wind across Pudding Lane that blows nobody any good, and the Great Fire that consumed huge swathes of the capital proved to be the making of one small island in the Thames just off to the west.

In the aftermath of the conflagration, Berkshire stone was transported to London to help in the great rebuilding project. It was taken down from the quarries on barges past Monkey Island to the city. When the boats returned they were filled with rubble and spoil that had to be dumped somewhere.

One of the many Thames islands to receive this little bit of scorched and broken London was Monkey Island, which, at a single stroke, was raised comfortably above the river and supplied with the foundations on which building could commence.

That's not to say that the island was immediately snapped up by property developers. It was to be another 57 years before Charles Spencer, the Third Duke of Marlborough, bought the island after chancing upon it while attending nearby meetings of the shady Kit-Cat Club, and began dreaming up the follies he would place on it.

Crossing via the graceful arc of the narrow footbridge – built in 1949 so that the then owner's pregnant wife could reach the island safely – today's visitor is met by a prospect of calm, rather formalised serenity. Beyond the effusive welcome of the enormous weeping willow, beyond the well-tended lawns grazed by peacocks and Canada geese, beyond

the gardeners patiently watering the ornamental shrubberies, stand two equally effulgent but very different Palladian buildings, each in their own separate space and each exuding a sense of timeless solidity. If Spencer were to return today he would doubtless recognise the scene, though he might be somewhat surprised that his small private buildings have now grown into a sizeable hotel.

The hotel has snared its fair share of famous admirers. Edward VII and Queen Alexandra took tea on the lawns with their children and grandchildren (including the future George V, Edward VIII and George VI). Edward Elgar visited many times while composing his Violin Concerto in B Minor across the river at a house called The Hut. Dames Nellie Melba and Clara Butt both sang to guests here, while HG Wells would row up from his uncle's pub in Windsor to meet Rebecca West, with whom he later had a son. West found the atmosphere magical, and Monkey Island forms the setting for a great deal of her first novel *The Return of the Soldier*.

HOW TO GET THERE
Take the train to Maidenhead station, then the No 6 bus to the village of Bray (alighting at the village hall), from where it's a mile to Monkey Island, with access via a footbridge.

RECIPE OF THE WEEK
Spinach & Walnut-stuffed Mushrooms
Serves 2

Prepare 5 mins **Cook** 20 mins
4 large, flat portabella mushrooms
150g frozen essential Waitrose Whole Leaf Spinach
1 tsp olive oil
2 cloves garlic, finely chopped
25g (1oz) walnut pieces, chopped
2 tbsp soured cream
¼ tsp grated nutmeg
1 tbsp white breadcrumbs
2 tbsp grated extra-mature Cheddar

1. Preheat the oven to 200C/400F/gas 6. Remove the stalks from the mushrooms, placing the caps stalk-side-up in an oiled baking tin. Chop the stalks. Cook the spinach in a covered pan until defrosted, then drain thoroughly.
2. Heat the oil in a non-stick frying pan and add the chopped mushroom stalks and garlic. Cook for 2 minutes until soft and golden. Stir in the spinach, walnuts and soured cream. Season and add the nutmeg. Spoon the mixture onto the mushrooms. Scatter the breadcrumbs and grated cheese over the mushrooms and bake for 12–15 minutes until cooked through and browned on top. Serve with a tomato and red onion salad and crusty bread.
Recipe and photograph from Waitrose. More than 5,000 recipes can be found at www.waitrose.com/recipes

THIS WEEK'S TOP TIP
Kiss and work-out for Valentine's Day

BEAUTY
What's in a kiss? A lot more than you might imagine. For a start it involves 30 facial muscles, which tone your cheeks and jaw, smooth out wrinkles and boost circulation to the skin – bringing you out in a youthful blush. Kissing also increases saliva production, which neutralises mouth acids and can help re-mineralise teeth. And, finally, passionate kissing can burn 100 calories an hour. What are you waiting for?

ALL THINGS BRIGHT AND BEAUTIFUL
Catkins
When the landscape is at its bleakest and the weather at its worst, catkins are a reminder that it's an ill wind that blows nobody any good. They are actually flowers that are wind pollinated; their shape and the winter weather playing a part in the plant's lifecycle. Yellowy-green hazel catkins (or lambs' tails) are the most familiar, but look out too for pink-tinged alder catkins, red-tipped poplar catkins, silver-birch catkins and pussy willow *(above)* – the soft fluffy flowers of various species of willow.

DON'T QUOTE ME, BUT...
'You can only perceive real beauty in a person as they get older'
Anouk Aimée

Stat attack

On average we eat 3.8 portions of fruit and vegetables a day – short of the five recommended by the NHS and the World Health Organisation

Light takes 1.25 seconds to travel from the moon to earth

Ants outnumber humans by a million to one

'No, I said get him a cat flap...'

Teenage translator

Déjà boo
Wearing the same costume to the Halloween party as you wore last year

Dissociative Facebook identity disorder
Someone whose Facebook image and real-life image are completely at odds

High ten
For those occasions when a high five is simply not enough. To execute, take one high five and multiply by two. Use sparingly, for only the most awesome of moments

UNEXPECTED ANNIVERSARIES
BILLETS DOUX
February 2014 is the 597th anniversary of:
the first Valentine

The first Valentine was sent by Charles, Duke of Orléans, after he was taken captive by the English at Agincourt in 1415 *(pictured above)*. He was kept as a prisoner in London for 25 years and sent regular love poems to his wife, which are claimed as the first formal Valentines; one of them addresses her as *'Ma très douce Valentinée'*.

Valentines were sent in 18th- and 19th-century Britain, and were introduced to the US in the 1840s by a woman named Esther Howland after she received one from England. These days, a billion cards are sent each year worldwide, 85% of them by women.

PET OF THE MONTH
The house hen

Name: Susy Speckles (*Dutch Bantam*)
Owner's name: Christopher Strange
Best habit: Saying good morning
under the bedroom window at dawn
Worst habit: Pecking your hand
if she thinks you're taking her food
Likes: Sitting on the arm
of your garden seat while you
enjoy a cup of tea
Dislikes: Sleeping in the coop with
the other chickens
Personality:
Cocky! Definitely mother hen
Naughtiest moment:
Chasing the dog
Most human trait:
Eating breakfast in the kitchen and
has own Facebook page

TOP TECHIE TIP
Facebook and the privacy thing

What happens when you divulge
snippets of info about yourself on
Facebook, whether in a 'profile' entry,
a conversation thread or on a 'status'
update? The key to safer Facebook
use is all about keeping on top of your
'Account' and 'Privacy' settings,
to help you reveal as much or as little
data as you wish. Go to facebook.
com/help/privacy/basic-controls.

JOKE OF THE MONTH
**My mother-in-law has
been coming to my house
every Sunday for the
past 14 years. Next week I'm
going to let her in!**

sent in by Alan Sitton

HOW TO MAKE
A VALENTINE BED GARLAND

**This pretty garland is a great way
to show your love and appreciation
and will make any setting
immediately more romantic.
A shorter version makes a wonderful
Valentine's gift and card**

WHAT YOU'LL NEED
Red felt
Red sewing thread
Red rose petals (optional)

WHAT TO DO
1. Make a small heart template and cut
out as many red hearts as you can
from the felt. Aim for around 50.
2. Thread your sewing machine
with red sewing thread and stitch
without any fabric for approximately
20cm (8in), then stitch across your
first heart. Stitch without any
fabric for another 5cm (2in) or so,
before you sew the second heart,
and continue like this until all the
hearts have been joined together.

3. To finish, keep sewing for a further
20cm (8in) before you cut the thread.
The thread at each end will allow you
to attach the garland to a bed or a
wall, but you could simply lay it across
a table for a romantic dinner à deux,
or run it across your pillows or sofa.

TOP TIPS
If you don't want to use felt, any firm
red fabric will do, but don't use
anything that will fray, because the
joy of this garland is that it doesn't
need hemming. You could even use
red card or paper, or a cut-out of
a printed romantic poem. If you have
lots of time and can crochet, make
a collection of hearts and join them
together with chain stitch. As well as
the garland on the pillows, why not
collect red rose petals and lay these in
the shape of a heart on the bed (*see
above*). This would work equally well
on a floor or table, and combined with
the garland makes a romantic setting.

BRAIN EXERCISE

Give your grey matter a work-out

SUDOKU

The game of logic. Place each of the digits 1 to 9 in each row, column and 3x3 box. There is only one solution.

						5		7
				2		9		
	8				9	6		
	4	7	9					3
6			3		1			2
	3			7	8	4		
		9	2				8	
	7		4					
4		1						

GRAMMAR CHALLENGE

The Lynne Truss test Can you spot the errors in grammar, punctuation and spelling? See below for the correct version.

the magnificent nora ephron made me wish desparately to become a writer unfortunately she said everything i ever wanted to say with such wit freshness and directness that i put down my pen she had the best lines on feminism and nailed how women feel about ageing as she wrote in her book i feel bad about my neck and other thoughts on being a woman our faces are lies and our necks are the truth you have to cut open a redwood tree to see how old it is but you wooden have to if it had a neck

FEBRUARY'S GENERAL KNOWLEDGE QUIZ

1. The novel *Jaws* was first published this month in 1974. Who wrote it?
A. Stephen King, B. Peter Benchley,
C. Jack Ketchum, D. Robert Ludlum

2. Which country is hosting the 2018 Winter Olympics?
A. South Korea, B. Canada, C. Norway, D. Croatia

3. Who starred in the hit film *Groundhog Day*?
A. Chevy Chase, B. Bill Murray,
C. Dan Aykroyd, D. John Belushi

4. What was the name of the sheep, cloned by scientists in Scotland in 1996?
A. Molly, B. Dolly, C. Wally, D. Holly

5. What was the real name of Mark Twain, whose *Adventures of Huckleberry Finn* was published in the US this month in 1885?
A. George M Redmayne, B. Samuel L Clemens,
C. Wyatt J Courtney, D. Thomas V Flynn

6. Renaissance mathematician Nicolaus Copernicus was born in February 1473 in which country?
A. Italy, B. Sweden, C. Poland, D. Denmark

7. Who wrote the song *My Funny Valentine*?
A. Rodgers and Hart, B. Hoagy Carmichael,
C. Rodgers and Hammerstein, D. Jimmy Van Heusen

8. Who wrote the controversial novel *Myra Breckenridge,* published in February 1968?
A. Saul Bellow, B. John Updike,
C. Gore Vidal, D. Phillip Roth

9. *The William Tell Overture* composed by Gioachino Rossini (b. February 1792), was the theme tune to which TV Western series.?
A. *Bonanza*, B. *The Lone Ranger*,
C, *The Wild Wild West*, B *Alias Smith and Jones*

10. Which member of the Monty Python team (b. February 1942) directed *The Life of Brian*?
A. Graham Chapman B. Terry Jones,
C. Terry Gilliam, D. Eric Idle

The magnificent Nora Ephron made me wish desperately to become a writer. Unfortunately, she said everything I ever wanted to say with such wit, freshness and directness that I put down my pen. She had the best lines on feminism and nailed how women feel about ageing. As she wrote in her book *I Feel Bad About My Neck: And Other Thoughts on Being a Woman:* 'Our faces are lies and our necks are the truth. You have to cut open a redwood tree to see how old it is, but you wouldn't have to if it had a neck.'

3	7	2	8	6	5	1	9	4
5	9	6	3	1	4	2	7	8
1	8	4	9	7	2	6	5	3
9	4	8	7	2	6	5	3	1
2	5	7	1	4	3	8	6	9
6	3	1	5	8	9	4	2	7
7	2	9	6	5	1	3	8	4
8	6	3	2	9	7	4	1	5
4	1	5	4	3	8	9	2	6

ANSWERS
1. B, 2. A,
3. B, 4. B,
5. B, 6. C,
7. A, 8. C,
9. B, 10. B

FIVE Q&AS

Is South America a big country?
Yes – so big that, in fact, it's a continent. South America consists of 13 countries, bordered by the Atlantic and Pacific oceans, with the mighty Andes running the whole length. The continent is packed with astounding national and cultural wonders – the challenge is deciding where to begin.

Don't tell me I've got to see 13 countries in 15 days?
Just do the Big Three: Brazil, Argentina and Chile. They're neighbours, so moving between them doesn't involve too much travelling time – in fact, getting there is sometimes part of the fun. Who could resist the chance of a scenic cruise by catamaran from a beautiful Chilean lake to an elegant Argentine town, say?

Why choose those three?
Between them, they offer a mixture of natural wonders, history and living culture that gives you a flavour of everything that's distinctive, fascinating and thrilling about this passion-filled and beautiful continent.

What's the weather like?
The climate's generally pleasant, and the seasons are 'opposite' to ours, so summer runs roughly from December to February.

A little history?
The Spanish and the Portuguese established colonies in the 15th century, and it was not until the early 19th century that the South Americans won their independence from the Spanish throne. Although Simón Bolívar struggled to keep the countries united after the War of Independence, they soon drifted apart, and there followed years of political upheaval as the different states jostled for power.

In the 1980s, democratic rule became widespread, and nowadays, despite a move to the left, South America is still largely capitalist, and enjoying its best-ever economic growth. In 2008, the Union of South American Nations (USAN) was formed with the aim of achieving economic and political integration.

SOUTH AMERICAN ADVENTURE

Get a feel for the continent by visiting Brazil, Argentina and Chile, and experience a combination of spectacular mountains, freezing lakes and cosmopolitan city life

FOUR SIGHTS TO SEE

Christ the Redeemer
The magnificent 30-metre statue of Christ the Redeemer *(Cristo Redentor)* stands on top of 710-metre-high Corcovado Mountain, within the beautiful Tijuca Forest National Park overlooking Rio de Janeiro. This iconic statue was voted one of the Seven New Wonders of the World in 2007.

The Andean Lakes, Chile
This is the 'other Lake District', where deep blue mountain lakes are surrounded by snow-capped volcanoes, larch forests, waterfalls, rivers and hot springs. A word of warning – the crystal clear waters may tempt you to swim, but these lakes are glacial, and that means COLD! Hypothermia is a real risk for bathers.

The Iguassu Falls on the border of Brazil and Argentina

RIO DE JANEIRO
LAT. 23°S
LONG. 43°W

Does Saga go there?
Yes, see the South American Adventure tour at saga.co.uk/travel

New World wonder
The Art Deco statue of Christ the Redeemer; shop for colourful hats in the market (*above*)

Iguassu Falls
When she saw these amazing falls, it's reported that First Lady Eleanor Roosevelt exclaimed 'Poor Niagara!' And, indeed, they're taller than Niagara Falls, and twice as wide.

Look out for the swallows that nest behind the falls, safe from predators. You'll be amazed by their death-defying swoops through the crashing water.

Copacabana Beach, Rio de Janeiro
Go for a promenade among the beautiful people, along the famous four kilometre-long black and white pavement. Imagine it thronged with revellers during New Year's Eve celebrations... or the 1.3 million people who came to see the Rolling Stones play there in 2006.

THREE THINGS TO KNOW
Similar – but different
As with Argentina, Spanish is Chile's official language, whereas in Brazil, it's Portuguese. However, a smattering of holiday Spanish will do very nicely in all three countries and, of course, many of the people you'll meet will speak English.

Try the national specialities
In Argentina, you'll naturally want to try a steak (which will probably be as large as your head!).

Chileans tend to eat dinner very late, so fill the gap with '*onces*' – literally, 'elevenses' but more accurately afternoon tea – served at *Salons de Té* throughout the country.

And in Brazil, sip a *caipirinha*, the national cocktail, while enjoying tapas-style snacks called *salgadhinos*.

Seek out the culture
South America is rich in culture, and you'll find many excellent, free museums and galleries to visit. Some fascinating sights, however, are not so easy to find. For example, the Palacio Barolo in Buenos Aires is the very best place for panoramic views of the whole city, there's no sign on the front to identify the building. Make sure you know the address – Avenida de Mayo 1370 – and ask the guard on the front desk to direct you to the ticket kiosk.

TWO THINGS TO AVOID
Flashing the cash
South America is pretty safe – travellers will encounter only the same sort of petty crime that occurs in big cities the world over. So don't make life easy for pickpockets by waving your wallet around, wearing expensive jewellery or leaving your bag unzipped.

Being stuck without small change
Tips can't be added to credit card bills, so be sure to take some cash, the smallest denominations you can get: many small shops and kiosks don't carry much change. One trick to avoid getting stuck with large-denomination bills from an ATM is to withdraw odd amounts, such as 290 pesos.

ONE MUST-DO
Don't leave South America without seeing the tango. The passionate, sensual tango originated in Buenos Aires and was declared a UNESCO Intangible Cultural Heritage of Humanity in 2009. And there's no better place on earth to see it danced properly than in a Buenos Aires tango hall.

MARCH
2014

ON THE BEACH
Deal, Kent
Photograph by Saga Magazine
reader Doris Phillips

MARCH

1
Saturday
St David's Day

2
Sunday

3
Monday

4
Tuesday
Shrove Tuesday

5
Wednesday

6
Thursday
Exhibition The Vikings
British Museum, London (to June 22)

7
Friday

8
Saturday

9
Sunday

10
Monday

11
Tuesday

12
Wednesday
Comedy Miranda Hart: My What I Call Live Show
O$_2$ Arena, London (and on March 13)

13
Thursday

14
Friday

15
Saturday

16
Sunday

17
Monday
St Patrick's Day, Bank Holiday NI and ROI

18
Tuesday

Saga Magazine has everything you need to fill your days
Diary looking a bit empty this month? Pick up your copy of Saga and turn to the Out There pages.
Every month we give you details of events all over the country, from music festivals to literary
get-togethers, celebratory anniversaries and days out. We review the latest films and give you the lowdown
on what everyone's talking about – from plays, musicals and dance, to unmissable exhibitions.
And you can find even more online at **www.saga.co.uk/magazine**. To subscribe call 0800 056 1057
or go to **www.saga.co.uk/magazine-subscriptions**

19
Wednesday

20
Thursday

21
Friday

22
Saturday

23
Sunday

24
Monday

25
Tuesday

26
Wednesday

27
Thursday

28
Friday

29
Saturday

30
Sunday
Mother's Day
British Summer Time begins

31
Monday

DECADE BUSTERS	TURNING 70	TURNING 50
MARCH BIRTHDAYS	**Sir Ranulph Fiennes** *explorer*	**Elle Macpherson**
	Roger Daltrey *singer (The Who)*	*Australian model*
	Gabrielle Drake *actress*	**Prince Edward**
	TURNING 60	*Earl of Wessex*
	Jimmy Nail *actor*	
	Lesley-Anne Down *(right) actress*	

THIS WEEK'S TOP TIP
Plant a pot of lilies for summer

GARDENING

If you want a pot of scented lilies by your garden bench this summer, now's the time to act. Go through the bulb catalogues and make your choice – or start by choosing a suitable pot.

Either way, it's crucial to match the two. The pot needs to be tall enough to balance the height of the lilies, both visually and for stability. If you're planting up a big pot, put it in its final position before you start. Begin with a layer of drainage material – chunks of polystyrene are just as good as broken crocks.

Then add compost, bearing in mind bulbs should be covered by two and a half times their depth

in compost. Many bulbs are cup-shaped, making them prone to holding water and rotting. To avoid this, lay the bulbs on their sides and sit them on a layer of horticultural grit. Add stakes now to avoid spearing bulbs when propping up top-heavy flowers later on.

Fill the pot to within about 5cm (2in) of the top, to leave room for watering.

RECIPE OF THE WEEK
Piperade with Eggs, Tomatoes, Pepper & Chorizo
Serves 2

Prepare 10 mins **Cook** 15 mins

1 tbsp olive oil + 1 tsp
1 small red onion, thinly sliced
1 clove garlic, finely chopped
1 Waitrose Red Romano pepper, deseeded and thinly sliced
½ red chilli, deseeded and chopped
2 vine tomatoes, quartered and chopped
70g (2¾oz) chorizo, diced (optional)
4 medium Columbian Blacktail eggs, beaten
Chopped flat-leaf parsley, to garnish

1. Heat 1 tbsp of olive oil in a medium frying pan and add the onion, garlic, pepper and chilli and cook for 8–10 minutes on a low heat until soft and golden.
2. Stir in the tomatoes (and chorizo, if using) and season. Cook over a high heat for 3-4 minutes until any moisture evaporates. Set aside and keep warm.
3. Heat 1 tsp of oil in a small non-stick pan and add the beaten eggs and seasoning. Stir over a low heat until curds form and it is soft and creamy and not quite set. Stir the egg into the pepper mixture, scatter with chopped parsley and serve with sliced baguette and a green salad.
Recipe and photograph from Waitrose. More than 5,000 recipes can be found at www.waitrose.com/recipes

ALL THINGS BRIGHT AND BEAUTIFUL
Blackthorn
The frothy white blossom of the blackthorn is a common hedgerow sight in spring. The bushes flower before they produce leaves (an easy way to distinguish them from hawthorn at this time of year). Black stems give the bush its name. Later on, in a good year, they will be laden with sloes *(see November)* and the thorny reference becomes self-evident when you come to pick them.

DON'T QUOTE ME, BUT...
'Experience is simply the name we give our mistakes'
Oscar Wilde

No handicap to making money

Golf has gone global – and with it the popularity of everything associated with it. Here is our guide to early golfing paraphernalia

Golf may have its roots in **Scotland** but is growing fastest in China. There are forecast to be 20 million Chinese players by 2020 – a surge in popularity likely to drive up demand for antique golf clubs.

Most hickory-shafted clubs have some value but the top prices are paid for the really old ones. You'd be extremely lucky to find a club dating back to the 15th or 16th centuries, when the sport began. That might fetch more than £50,000. Clubs made after 1800, when the game took off, could also be worth thousands. A maker's name often determines price. Philp, McEwan and Morris are among those to look out for.

Post-1900 clubs are less desirable since they were produced in much larger quantities. Interest diminishes still further after 1925 when steel shafts were introduced. It's around

SOLD
This feathery, thought to be 200 years old, was sold by Mullock's of Ludlow for £1,444.80 in April 2013

this time that clubs started to have numbers rather than evocative names like Brassie, Mashie, Cleek and Jigger. Early golf balls can also be worth thousands, especially 'featheries' – made from feathers and leather.

REDISCOVERED BOOK

'One of the classic accounts of life in the English countryside'

Corduroy
Adrian Bell
(Slightly Foxed Paperback, £11)

Adrian Bell was a rather frail young man of 20 when, in 1920, he left the bohemian life of London to work on a Suffolk farm. Out of that experience he wrote *Corduroy*, one of the classic accounts of life in the English countryside. *Corduroy* is filled with precise and poetic descriptions of the countryside and of farming life. It is not simply a period piece – it captures what is unchanging about the lives of those who live from, rather than simply on, the land.

As chosen by the staff of Slightly Foxed bookshop, specialists in unusual titles, old and new; www.foxedbooks.com

'Once I'd tried on those clothes at your grandmother's, I knew there was no going back.'

RECIPE OF THE WEEK
Keralan Fish Curry
Serves 4

Prepare 10 mins **Cook** 15 mins

700g (1lb 8oz) Waitrose Line Caught Prime
Icelandic Haddock Fillets (in packs or from
the service counter), skinned and cubed
2 tsp ground turmeric
Vegetable oil spray
2 onions, thinly sliced
1 tsp cumin or black mustard seeds (or ½ tsp of each)
400ml can essential Waitrose Half-Fat Coconut Milk
1 tbsp Waitrose Cooks' Ingredients Tamarind Paste
5cm (2in) piece fresh ginger, shredded
225g (8oz) trimmed mangetout, halved lengthways
2 salad onions, thinly sliced
2 red chillies, seeded and thinly sliced

1. Sprinkle the fish with the turmeric and set aside.
2. Spray a large pan with oil and cook the onions with the
cumin and/or mustard seeds for 5-10 minutes until golden.
Add the coconut milk, tamarind paste and shredded
ginger and bring to a simmer.
3. Add the fish and mangetout to the pan; cover and
simmer gently for 3-4 minutes until the fish is cooked.
Scatter with sliced salad onions and chillies and serve with
brown basmati rice.
Recipe and photograph from Waitrose. More than 5,000
recipes can be found at www.waitrose.com/recipes

THIS WEEK'S TOP TIP
Make sure you get enough **Vitamin D**

HEALTH
Vitamin D is protective against many
conditions, and now scientists from
University College, London have found that
it can rejuvenate ageing eyes. As we
get older it gets harder for the body
to make its own supply, which is why the
Government wants GPs to advise
everyone over 65 to take a supplement.
'A significant proportion of people in
the UK probably have inadequate levels
of vitamin D in their blood,'
says the UK's Chief Medical Officer.

ALL THINGS BRIGHT AND BEAUTIFUL
Wild garlic
When you're out walking in the woods, it's more than likely
that you'll smell wild garlic before you spot it, which is
one of the reasons it's so safe to forage for, as it really
is unmistakable. It's easy to pick handfuls of the long green
leaves and take them home to add to a risotto or to make
a version of pesto. Just make sure you pick them well away
from roads, or footpaths frequented by dogs. For best
flavour, pick before the plant has flowered. And discard
any other leaves that you may have grabbed at the
same time – if it doesn't smell of garlic, don't eat it.

DON'T QUOTE ME, BUT...
'I refuse to admit I'm more than 52, even if that does make my sons illegitimate'
Nancy Astor

BADGER'S BLOG
'I HAVE AN UNEASY TRUCE WITH BIRDS'

Badger finds that she and the local
birds are united in their dislike of cats

I've been busy digging a really big hole in the lawn. This always makes GOB fall over laughing, and BOG come running out of the house with a red face, shouting and waving his arms about. This makes me laugh as well.

HARARRRRUFF! I bide my time patiently while he's hobbling around the grass in his special spiky shoes and carefully sprinkling some seed around. After that, it's a race between me and the birds to see who can get there first to undo all his hard work.

I have an uneasy truce with birds, because they hate cats even more than I do and… Grrr… I really hate those mangy furballs. So the idea that someone hates them more than me makes me very happy. 'My enemy's enemy is my friend' as we say in higher dognitive circles.

Every year around this time the birds and I have a summit. I agree not to chase them off the lawn if they agree to tell me the moment they see a furball sneaking furtively in the direction of my garden. One time they

didn't tell me and a dozy kitten called Bob from the new neighbours ambled innocently in through the back door while the humans were reading the papers and I was having a snooze. Time stood still for a moment as we all looked at Bob grinning at us like an idiot. I have to admit that I was so surprised that I was a bit slow off the mark. BOG jumped on me as GOB shooed Bob out of the kitchen. He still didn't get the message so I wriggled free and taught him a valuable lesson in self-preservation.

What would I have done if I'd caught him? IF? Let's get something straight. I could have caught him if I'd wanted to, but I'm not completely without feeling when it comes to juvenile furballs, so he might not have gone quite the same way as the rubber chicken. But there are no guarantees in this dog-eat-cat world.

Nickname for me this month?
Pupskin Puckarooka. GRRR.
Best moment: *Chased Bob up a tree. The window cleaner had to get him down.*

Neighbourhood watch, dog-style – on the look out for cats

RECIPE OF THE WEEK
Leek, Potato & Stilton Omelette
Serves 4

Prepare 10 mins **Cook** 20 mins
500g (1lb) bag Waitrose Roseval potatoes, thickly sliced
400g (14oz) leeks, sliced
8 medium free-range eggs
1 tbsp chopped rosemary
1 tbsp olive oil
100g (4oz) Waitrose Long Clawson Creamy Blue Stilton

1. Cook the potatoes in a large pan of boiling water for 5 minutes. Add the leeks and cook for another 2 minutes, then drain well.
2. Crack the eggs in a large bowl and beat together. Stir in the drained vegetables and the rosemary.
3. Heat the oil in a large non-stick frying pan and pour in the egg mixture. Crumble the cheese over the egg and cook over a gentle heat for 12-15 minutes, until almost cooked through.
4. Pop under a preheated grill for a further 5 minutes or so until golden brown and completely set. Cut into wedges and serve warm.
Recipe and photograph from Waitrose. More than 5,000 recipes can be found at www.waitrose.com/recipes

THIS WEEK'S TOP TIP
Top up your ISA

MONEY
Don't forget to make any savings or investments by the end of the tax year, April 5. Check the current limits that you can put into a cash ISA and/or a stocks and shares ISA at hmrc.gov.uk (type ISA in the search box). If you want to switch providers, ask your new provider for a transfer form. If you're switching this year's cash ISA, you have to put the entire amount into the new ISA – you can't split it. The same applies when moving this year's stocks and shares ISA. The rules are more flexible when you're transferring ISAs from past years.

ALL THINGS BRIGHT AND BEAUTIFUL
Hares
Although superficially similar to rabbits, hares are much bigger and can look even more so thanks to their habit of standing up tall on their hind legs. If you're still in doubt, check the tips of their ears: hares have distinctive dark tips. Mad March hares 'boxing' in the fields are typically a male and female, with the female being not quite so interested in mating. Unlike rabbits, hares don't burrow. Young hares or leverets are reared in a 'form', a shallow depression in the grass, and rely on camouflage to keep them safe.

DON'T QUOTE ME, BUT...
'As you get older three things happen. The first is your memory goes. I can't remember the other two'
Norman Wisdom

KING OF THE SHIP
The pub landlord rules this island off the coast of Cumbria

PIEL ISLAND
Nr Barrow-in-Furness, Cumbria
Size: 52 acres
Population: 4

If you were going to design an ideal island from scratch it's very likely you'd come up with Piel. It comprises one pub, one short terrace of Victorian houses, a beach, a lake, plentiful seabirds and, naturally, one medieval castle. It's accessible via a ten-minute ride on a tiny ferry or a mile-and-a-half walk over the sands at low tide from another nearby island, Walney.

The view from Piel is nothing short of extraordinary: a panorama stretches all the way from Barrow up to the Lake District's forbidding Black Coombe, around a panoply of hills to the Old Man of Coniston, down to the long sweep of the Fylde coast and all the way to the Blackpool Tower. If all this were not enough, the island also happens to have been the scene of the last invasion of Britain.

Jumping off at Piel's impressively slippery jetty, the first sight is the welcoming one of the Ship Inn. Difficult though it is to believe on an island with a population of four, there are regulars here. Kayakers and the crews of an assortment of boats moor up throughout the evening and stride in, as though paddling or sailing to one's local were the most natural thing in the world. Another thing treated as perfectly normal in these parts is that the landlord is also the King of Piel.

The tradition of crowning the landlord of the island's pub is a slightly murky one. As far as can be established, it began in the early 19th century in mocking reference to the attempt to put Lambert Simnel on the throne of England. On June 4, 1487, the pretender to the throne – a lad just ten years old – landed with several thousand mercenaries under the command of Colonel Martin Schwartz. Though of course they didn't know it at the time, they were en route to ignominious defeat at the hands of Henry VII's army at the Battle of Stoke Field in Nottinghamshire.

To commemorate this rather dismal chapter in English history, each successive landlord of the Ship sits on a special wooden throne wearing a ceremonial helmet and brandishing a sword. A large quantity of alcohol is then poured over him and he is proclaimed king.

In 1920, at the instigation of the mayor of Barrow, the Duke of Buccleuch presented the island to the town of Barrow-in-Furness as a memorial to the dead of The First World War. The name of the mayor was Alfred Barrow. Gone are the days when every mayor had to bear the name of his home town and we're all the poorer for it.

HOW TO GET THERE
Take the train to Roose, then the no 11 bus to Roa Island. The Piel Island Ferry sails from 11am to 6pm, weather permitting. Alternatively, travel to Barrow-in-Furness station and board the no 2 bus from Duke Street to Walney Island, hike the six miles to Snab Point and walk to Piel at low tide. Warning: there have been some reports of sinking sands.

THIS WEEK'S TOP TIP
Fed up with looking pale and interesting?

BEAUTY
While you're in the shower, gently slap your cheeks. The resulting rush of blood to the face helps tone it up and you'll step out of the bathroom looking as if you've just come back from a morning run. Lips and eyes lose definition as we age, so try using a slightly brighter shade of lipstick than you would normally – it can stop tired skin looking grey too. Try navy mascara to bring out the whites of your eyes and make them sparkle.

DON'T QUOTE ME, BUT...

'One should never trust a woman who tells her real age. If she tells that, she'll tell anything'
Oscar Wilde

RECIPE OF THE WEEK
Sticky Honey, Almond & Banana Cake
Makes 12 slices

Prepare 10 mins **Cook** 35 mins
125g (4½oz) self-raising flour
50g (2oz) ground almonds
100g (4oz) butter, cubed
100g (4oz) light muscovado sugar
150g (5oz) Rowse Squeezy Light and Mild Honey
1 ripe banana, mashed
2 medium free-range eggs, beaten
25g (1oz) flaked almonds

1. Preheat the oven to 180C/350F/gas 4. Grease and base-line a 28cm x 18cm (11in x 7in) tin.
2. Sift the flour into a mixing bowl and stir in the ground almonds. Place the butter, sugar and honey in a small pan and heat gently until completely melted. Remove from the heat and leave to cool for a few minutes.
3. Add the melted ingredients to the flour and almonds, and add the banana and beaten eggs. Beat well to give a smooth mixture and pour into the prepared tin. Level the surface and scatter with the flaked almonds. Bake for 30-35 minutes until well risen and firm to touch. Turn onto a wire rack to cool. Serve cut into 12 squares.
Recipe and photograph from Waitrose. More than 5,000 recipes can be found at www.waitrose.com/recipes

ALL THINGS BRIGHT AND BEAUTIFUL
Ladybirds
Ladybirds overwinter as adults, emerging from hibernation as the weather warms up to look for food, mate and lay eggs. Throughout its lifetime – typically a year – a ladybird can eat thousands of greenfly, both as an adult and in the grub-like larval stage, so they're invaluable gardeners' allies. There are 46 species of these small beetles in the UK – pictured above is a familiar two-spot ladybird.

UNEXPECTED ANNIVERSARIES
SPEARED!
March 2014 is the 191st anniversary of:
the Rostocker Pfeilstorch

Until the 1820s, nobody knew where all the migratory birds disappeared to in the winter. It was thought by some that they hibernated, perhaps underwater, or even turned into mice.

Samuel Johnson, for example, wrote that: 'Swallows certainly sleep in the winter. A number of them conglobulate together by flying round and round, and then all in a heap throw themselves under water, and lye on the bed of the river.'

However, in 1822 a northwards-migrating stork turned up in Germany, near a village called Klütz, with an African arrow through its neck – and people realised it must have been shot in Africa and flown north. The stuffed bird is in a museum at the University of Rostock, complete with its arrow.

'You've **always** got a headache.'

WOTEVA!
Teenage translator

Powerpuff presentation
A presentation that is full of animation and fancy graphics but completely devoid of any substance

Premake
The original version of a song that a modern band has remade or redone. The teen will often doubt the existence of the premake

Screen saver
The blank and sometimes blissful expression that may come across a person's face when they are daydreaming

PET OF THE MONTH

PET OF THE MONTH
Cuddle me

Name: Teddy
Owners' names:
Flora and Alice Midgley
Best habit: Always pleased to see you
Worst habit: Chewing through
wires – landline cut off, laptop lead
and two phone chargers ruined
Likes: Human company
and food – any food
Dislikes: Being trodden on when you
haven't spotted he's under your feet
Personality: Indecisive – never knows
if he wants to be in or out
Naughtiest moment: Pooing in
lovingly tended seed trays
Most human trait: Loves a cuddle

TOP TECHIE TIP
The data game

**You have stacks of digital content on
your computer and smartphone, but
how much of it do you actually own?**
Not much, if any, will be pretty near
the mark. So what will eventually
happen to your, shall we say, 'digital
legacy'? Here are a couple of common
examples. When you buy a track from
iTunes, this means you've purchased
a licence for the music, not the music
itself. But you could pass on your
usernames and passwords for your
account, or leave that music to
someone of your choice if it's stored
on a device. As for books, Amazon's
terms forbid the transfer of e-books
between devices, unlike a physical
library. But you can leave your
e-books on your Kindle, for example,
and family members with access
to your Amazon account will be able
to access your digital content.

HOW TO MAKE
HOME-MADE CARDS

**It is far nicer to receive a handmade
card than a bought one: it
has the added attraction of being
personalised and individual,
and you may even be saving trees
at the same time**

Cards can also be very quick to
make. If you have the right materials
to hand, it is possible to produce
a card in minutes, so always squirrel
away anything that catches your eye
and you'll soon have an archive of
materials to work with. Some of the
ideas above – such as the playing
card attached with photo corners, or
the small card of vintage buttons
– are inspirations for using interesting
things you already have. Other ideas
include using woven name tapes
saying 'Happy Christmas', for example
– a simple tip but one that needs
some planning ahead (tapes can be
ordered from companies that produce
name labels for children's clothes and
can be ready in a few days).

GETTING IDEAS – REUSE, RECYCLE
Look out for old books, sheet music
and vintage magazines in markets;
these are great for card-making
as well as for gift-wrapping. Search
out vintage playing cards too –
the decorative sides are often themed
and can look wonderful attached to
a blank card. If you want something
more elaborate, you can stitch
together a few cards to spell out
a name or word (use cards featuring
letters or cut cards into letter
shapes), that can then be folded,
concertina-style, and posted.

And remember you can also use
all your card ideas in miniature
for making personalised gift tags.

JOKE OF THE MONTH
A policeman spots a woman
driving and knitting at the same
time. Driving up beside her,
he says: 'Pull over!'
'No,' she shouts back, 'a pair of socks!'

sent in by Mary Bowen

USE IT OR LOSE IT
BRAIN EXERCISE
Give your grey matter a work-out

SUDOKU
The game of logic. Place each of the digits 1 to 9 in each row, column and 3x3 box. There is only one solution.

			8	6			9	
	5	3	9					
2	1							
6		4				5		
5	9						7	1
		1				2		9
							6	7
			2	3	8			
	6			7	5			

GRAMMAR CHALLENGE
The Lynne Truss test Can you spot the errors in grammar, punctuation and spelling? See below for the correct version.

we support each other she said which is terribly important i think they divide their time between london los angeles and wherever either of them happen to be making a movie trying not to let the inevitable seperations last for two long six or seven weeks is kind of ok she once told me but when its three months then that gets difficult the worst thing is that you get used to being apart and then when your together its like who did you say you are again oh goodness yes your my husband

MARCH'S GENERAL KNOWLEDGE QUIZ

1. March is named after the Roman god of war. Which planet follows Mars in Gustav Holst's *Planet Suite*?
A. Venus, B. Saturn, C. Jupiter, D. Mercury.

2. Mars Bonfire wrote which classic rock anthem?
A. *Light My Fire*, B. *Born to Be Wild*,
C. *Eternal Flame*, D. *Hot Rails to Hell*.

3. In Jonathan Miller's 1966 BBC production of *Alice in Wonderland*, who played the March Hare?
A. John Cleese, B. Michael Gough,
C. Alan Bennett, D. Peter Cook.

4. Failing to heed the 'ides of March', Julius Caesar was killed by his enemies. But in Shakespeare's play, who strikes the first blow?
A. Cinna, B. Cassius, C. Casca, D. Brutus.

5. In which city was legendary escapologist Harry Houdini born in March 1874?
A. London, B. New York, C. Warsaw, D. Budapest

6. What was the real name of the *Middlemarch* author who wrote under the pen name George Eliot?
A. Mary Anne Evans, B. Mary Shelley,
C. Mary Jones, D. Mary Hall.

7. The lyric 'If I ruled the world, every day would be the first day of spring' comes from which musical?
A. *Micawber*, B, *Pickwick*, C. *Oliver*, D. *Copperfield*.

8. In *The Great Escape*, based on the 1944 break-out from Stalag Luft III, which actor makes it to freedom?
A, James Coburn, B, Nigel Stock,
C. David McCallum, D. Steve McQueen.

9. Which football club was founded in March 1892?
A. Blackburn Rovers, B. Liverpool, C. Crystal Palace, D. Leeds Utd.

10. Who replaced Eric Clapton (b. March 1945) as guitarist in John Mayall's Bluesbreakers in 1965?
A. Mick Green, B. Peter Green,
C. Mick Taylor, D. Ron Wood.

'We support each other,' she said, 'which is terribly important,' I think. They divide their time between London, Los Angeles and wherever either of them happens to be making a movie, trying not to let the inevitable separations last for too long. 'Six or seven weeks is kind of OK,' she once told me, 'but when it's three months then that gets difficult. The worst thing is that you get used to being apart, and then when you're together it's like, "Who did you say you are again? Oh goodness, yes, you're my husband."'

ANSWERS
1. A, **2.** B,
3. B, **4.** C,
5. D, **6.** A,
7. B, **8.** A,
9. B, **10.** B

9	8	6	1	7	5	4	2	3
1	7	4	6	2	3	8	9	5
3	5	2	9	4	8	1	6	7
3	1	5	8	9	2	7	4	6
5	6	9	8	2	3	4	7	1
6	2	4	7	1	9	5	3	8
2	9	1	4	5	7	3	8	6
4	8	6	9	3	6	7	1	2
2	5	6	1	9	8	3	7	4

TASMANIA

Overlooked for years by Australia's tourism industry, and once shackled to its penal past, the so-called 'island at the end of the world' is now one of the hottest spots to visit in the southern hemisphere

FIVE Q&As

Where on earth is it? Tasmania really is on the edge of the inhabited world – Latitude 42°S, Longitude 147°E. In plain English, this island (about the size of Ireland) is 150 miles south of the Australian mainland, with nothing between it and Antarctica but more than 3,000 miles of Southern Ocean. They get some rough seas down there.

Does that mean the weather's lousy? If you go during their summer season between late October and April, it's remarkably like home (but in reverse). Unlike the mainland, it has a mild maritime climate. So the answer is: sometimes yes, sometimes no.

So what's the point of travelling halfway around the world? For its unspoilt sprawling temperate rainforests and natural beauty. When the island applied for UNESCO World Heritage status, it met seven out of ten of the criteria for selection. That's more than any other World Heritage site. Tasmania now has 19 vast national parks and nearly 40% of the island is protected wilderness. In large parts of the island it is possible to believe that this really is what the world would look like without the interference of man.

There must be some bright lights? Don't imagine that it's all wilderness. Hobart, its vibrant riverside capital, is home to nearly a quarter of a million people. Its unique architectural heritage of convict-built sandstone Georgian warehouses has

been restored and redeveloped as a fashionable creative quarter with studios, galleries, cafés, 'art' hotels, and some of the best new restaurants in the country. Salamanca Place is the focal point of all this energy.

A 30-second history? It was separated from the mainland 10,000 years ago when sea levels rose, isolating its aboriginal people from the rest of mankind. It didn't do them much good. They were all but wiped out by disease or the bullet when Europeans arrived in numbers in the 18th century. Tasmania was originally known as Van Diemen's Land, after

the governor of the Dutch East Indies who commissioned the first exploration of the Southern Ocean in 1642. But by popular consent the colony's name was changed to Tasmania in 1856 in recognition of the Dutch explorer Abel Tasman, the first European to land on its shores more than two centuries earlier. The islanders felt the original name had too many negative associations with its notorious penal colony. 'Tas' or 'Tassie', became a full Australian state in 1901. It now ranks in the official top five of the country's tourist attractions, up there with Sydney and the Great Barrier Reef.

TASMANIA
LAT. 42°S
LONG. 147°E

Natural history
Dove Lake (*main*), Hobart harbour
(*left*) and wildflowers (*below*)

Launceston. Northern Tasmania's largest city is an intriguing mix of classic Victoriana and contemporary chic. It's also the home of Tasmania's best brewery, Boag's.

THREE THINGS TO KNOW

Screen legend Errol Flynn was born in Hobart in 1909.

The island is home to the world's only carnivorous marsupial – the endangered Tasmanian devil. Proportionate to its size, about that of a small dog, it has more powerful jaws than any other living mammal – exerting a bite force of 1,220lbs.

The thylacine (or Tasmanian tiger), the largest known marsupial carnivore, was declared extinct in 1936. But in 1982 a wildlife officer claimed to have spotted one.

TWO THINGS TO AVOID

Huntsman spiders. They can grow to the size of a human hand and are very hairy – but harmless.

Wildlife crossing the road. 'Roadkill' is a common sight, mainly because there are an awful lot of animals foraging at night on unlit roads.

ONE MUST-DO

The Freycinet Experience Walk A peninsula jutting south into the Tasman Sea, where you might not see another living soul except albatross, sea eagles, pelicans, black swans and tame wallabies.

Does Saga go there?
Yes, find out more about travel to Tasmania at
saga.co.uk/holidays

FOUR SIGHTS TO SEE

Strahan (pr. 'Strawn') is a delightful fishing village on the western coast. From here take a cruise down the Gordon River, deep into the heart of the rainforest, or board a seaplane for the same journey weaving through ancient myrtles, leatherwoods, and Huon pines 150ft tall. It'll be the best ride of your life.

Dove Lake, Cradle Mountain Walk the 6km circuit around this tranquil mountain lake and find yourself in the enchanting Ballroom Forest – so-called because the old lichen-draped trees look as though they're frozen in an embrace, mid-dance.

Board a seaplane weaving through ancient myrtles for the ride of your life

In MONA (the Museum of Old and New Art) Hobart has one of the world's most innovative (and infamous) private museums, built on three levels underground. It has been described as a 'subversive adult Disneyland'. Some of the exhibits really have to be seen to be believed. And even then you still won't believe them.

APRIL
2014

A SEA OF BLUE
Norsey Wood, Essex
Photograph by Saga Magazine
reader Neil Park

APRIL

1
Tuesday

2
Wednesday

3
Thursday

4
Friday

5
Saturday
The Grand National, Aintree

6
Sunday

7
Monday

8
Tuesday

9
Wednesday

10
Thursday

11
Friday

12
Saturday

13
Sunday

14
Monday

15
Tuesday

16
Wednesday

17
Thursday
(e vent) **Art Henri Matisse: The Cut-Outs**
Tate Modern, Bankside, London (to Sept 7)

18
Friday
Good Friday

Saga Magazine has everything you need to fill your days

Diary looking a bit empty this month? Pick up your copy of Saga and turn to the Out There pages. Every month we give you details of events all over the country, from music festivals to literary get-togethers, celebratory anniversaries and days out. We review the latest films and give you the lowdown on what everyone's talking about – from plays, musicals and dance, to unmissable exhibitions. And you can find even more online at **www.saga.co.uk/magazine**. To subscribe call 0800 056 1057 or go to **www.saga.co.uk/magazine-subscriptions**

19
Saturday

20
Sunday

21
Monday
Easter Monday

22
Tuesday

23
Wednesday
St George's Day

24
Thursday

25
Friday

26
Saturday

27
Sunday

28
Monday

29
Tuesday

30
Wednesday

DECADE BUSTERS

APRIL
BIRTHDAYS

TURNING 70
John Sergeant *broadcaster*
Hywel Bennett *actor*

TURNING 60
Iain Duncan Smith *politician*
Jerry Seinfeld *American comedian*

TURNING 50
Fiona Bruce *(above) TV newsreader*
Lady Helen Taylor
  member of the Royal Family
Russell Crowe *New Zealander actor*

RECIPE OF THE WEEK
British Rhubarb, Macadamia & White Chocolate Cake
Makes 12 slices

Prepare 15 mins **Cook** 35-40 mins

250g (9oz) plain flour
2 tsp baking powder
1 tsp bicarbonate of soda
1 tsp cinnamon
100g (4oz) butter
125g (4½oz) golden caster sugar
2 medium essential Waitrose Free-Range Eggs
150g (5oz) natural yogurt
400g (14oz) essential Waitrose Rhubarb,
*   cut into 2.5cm (1in) lengths*
50g (2oz) macadamia nuts, roughly chopped
50g (2oz) white chocolate, broken into small chunks

1. Preheat the oven to 180C/350F/gas 4. Sift 200g (7oz) of the flour with the baking powder, bicarbonate of soda and the cinnamon into a large mixing bowl. Rub in 75g (3oz) of the butter until the mixture looks like coarse breadcrumbs and stir in 100g (4oz) of the sugar. Beat the eggs with the yogurt, then beat into the dry ingredients to make a soft mixture.

2. Spoon the cake mixture into a buttered and base-lined baking tin, about 28cm x 18cm x 4cm (11in x 7in x 1½in), and smooth the surface. Top with the rhubarb. Rub the remaining butter and flour together and stir in the rest of the sugar. Add the chopped macadamia nuts and the white chocolate chunks. Scatter over the rhubarb.

3. Bake for 35-40 minutes until well risen and a skewer inserted into the centre of the cake comes out clean. Turn onto a wire rack to cool. Serve warm with Waitrose Seriously Creamy Madagascan Vanilla Ice Cream or leave to cool and store in an airtight container.
Recipe and photograph from Waitrose. More than 5,000 recipes can be found at www.waitrose.com/recipes

THIS WEEK'S TOP TIP
Give your lawn a makeover

GARDENING
Start by creating a cleanly defined edge to your lawn – it makes a big difference to the overall appearance of the garden (along with neatly swept paths).

There's no need to buy a special edging tool, a spade will do just as well. A piece of wood as a guide will give you a professional straight edge. Then dig out dandelions and creeping buttercups (and daisies if you don't like them) – use a two-pronged daisy grubber or an old, sharp vegetable knife. Then reseed the bare patches.

Loosen the soil, then mix some grass seed with some potting compost and scatter it over. Firm it down gently before watering with a fine rose attachment. In warm weather it will be growing within weeks.

Cut newly seeded patches by hand with shears once the grass is about 5cm (2in) tall. After that, it should be able to tolerate regular mowing.

ALL THINGS BRIGHT AND BEAUTIFUL
Cuckoo
Hearing the first cuckoo of the year as it arrives from Africa is a defining spring moment. But it's one that we're hearing less frequently as their populations decline.

Cuckoos are probably best known for their unusual lifestyle – laying eggs in other birds' nests and letting them do all the hard work. Research has shown that individual cuckoos tend to favour one species to act as host.

DON'T QUOTE ME, BUT...
'Age and guile beat youth, innocence and a bad haircut'
PJ O'Rourke

Cooking the books

Take a look at that old recipe book your granny gave you – it could be a valuable classic. Read on for the ingredients of a good first edition

The constant diet of food programmes on television has stimulated interest in a wide range of cookery writing, from 18th-century chefs explaining how to serve up calves' heads to Delia Smith on how to avoid sagging soufflés. Early cookery books from the 1700s to 1850s can fetch thousands and even modern books can sell for many hundreds, depending on edition and condition.

Isabella Beeton wrote her classic *Mrs Beeton's Book of Household Management* in her early twenties and died when only 28. An 1861 first edition of the book in good condition might make £1,500. Her comments about servants are as revealing as her recipes. She advises, for example, that a servant should never say good night or good morning 'except in reply to that salutation'.

Fast forward a hundred years and there are other classics to look out for. Elizabeth David wrote her influential *French Provincial Cookery* in 1960. A first edition with a good dust jacket would fetch several

SOLD

Like cookery books, old children's books are often the worse for wear. But despite their somewhat tatty appearance, this first edition set of *The Chronicles of Narnia* by CS Lewis made £4,875 at Sotheby's in December 2010

hundred pounds. A year later Julia Child, played in 2009 by Meryl Streep in the film *Julie and Julia*, co-wrote *Mastering the Art of French Cooking,* which is equally desirable.

REDISCOVERED BOOK

'A truly uplifting book: happy endings do exist'

Enchanted April
Elizabeth von Arnim
(Virago £7.99)

On the spur of the moment, on a wet and dismal day, slight acquaintances Rose and Lottie, decide to rent a castle in Italy. Unable to afford the rent, they advertise for companions. Thus it is that four women, dissatisfied with life for a variety of reasons, travel to Italy for the month of April. The country, the castle and its owner all work their charms and everyone's lives are improved. A truly uplifting book: happy endings do exist.

As chosen by the staff of Slightly Foxed bookshop, specialists in unusual titles old and new. www.foxedbooks.com

'No kidding... Tesco, eh...'

RECIPE OF THE WEEK
Warm Chicken & Bean Salad with Wholegrain Mustard Dressing
Serves 4

Prepare 10 mins **Cook** 10 mins

400g (14oz) Waitrose British Chicken Breast Chunks
2 sprigs rosemary, finely chopped
2 garlic cloves, finely chopped
2 tbsp olive oil
280g (10oz) Waitrose Fine Green Beans, trimmed
400g can essential Waitrose Butter Beans,
    drained and rinsed
2 tbsp Maille Wholegrain Mustard
1 tbsp clear honey
1 tbsp white wine vinegar
1 red onion, very thinly sliced
Sliced baguette, to serve

1. Toss together the chicken, rosemary, garlic and ½ tbsp of the olive oil. Heat a large non-stick frying pan and cook the chicken for 10 minutes until tender and golden brown.
2. Meanwhile, cook the green beans in a large pan of boiling water for 2 minutes, then add the butter beans and cook for a further 2 minutes until the green beans are tender and the butter beans are heated through. Drain well.
3. Whisk together the remaining 1½ tbsp oil, the mustard, honey and vinegar.
4. In a large serving bowl, mix together the warm chicken and beans, mustard dressing and red onions. Serve warm with slices of baguette.
Recipe and photograph from Waitrose. More than 5,000 recipes can be found at www.waitrose.com/recipes

THIS WEEK'S TOP TIP
Watching TV is good for you...

HEALTH
...but only if you watch old favourites. Researchers in the US found that watching reruns on TV can give you an extra boost of energy and mental stimulation to tackle difficult tasks, especially when you feel you've used up all your reserves. The effect is limited to watching shows with which you're familiar – watching whatever happens to be on TV or even a new episode of a favourite series doesn't have the same effect.
Researchers think the effect is due to the show's familiarity: you're not having to exert much mental energy because you know what's going to happen, yet you're enjoying interacting with your favourite characters. The result: a swift restoration of your mental powers.

ALL THINGS BRIGHT AND BEAUTIFUL
Primroses
'Primrosing', picking bunches of flowers to give to family and friends, to decorate the church, or even to sell, was a family pastime that died out in the conservation-minded Seventies. Yet there is no conclusive research to show that simply picking (rather than digging up whole plants) affects colonies. Primrose Day is on April 19, the anniversary of Disraeli's death; posies are laid on his grave.

DON'T QUOTE ME, BUT...
'True terror is to wake up one morning and discover that your high-school class is running the country'
Kurt Vonnegut

BADGER'S BLOG
'DID I MENTION MY PARENTS?'

In which we get the lowdown on Badger's pedigree – plus a howling success

Other things start happening in the garden this month. Bigger holes are dug in the lawn and some of my favourite old bones and soggy chews are recovered from the flower beds. Sometimes we discover forgotten treasures such as slippers, socks, gloves, washing-up brushes, spectacles, remote controls, and on one memorable occasion, a mobile phone.

BOG was particularly happy about discovering the last one, until he couldn't make it work. Then I had to hide in the bushes until he calmed down. Once he tripped over me when he came outside to find out where I was, and landed on his kneecap on the patio. I thought dogs could howl, but I learnt something new that night. AAARRRRAAARROO OOOWHHHAROOO!!!

Talking of howling, my dog mother and I often have a good session, flexing our vocal cords to ensure we stay in touch. My dog dad sometimes joins in, if he's not out on something called 'the razzle'. Then the foxhounds start up from their kennels on the other side of the valley. Often BOG and GOB and the neighbours also add their own loud human cries of 'Shurrup!' It can get very noisy at night in the countryside.

Did I mention my dog parents? I'm practically aristocracy round here. Mum's a pedigree Golden Lab called Sandy, Dad's a well-known Lurcher called Ollie who lives in a caravan on a nearby farm. He is famous for being 'heroically reproductive', according to BOG. I don't know what this means, but I do know that Sandy's owner wasn't too happy when Ollie paid her a visit one night. That was about three months before me and the dimwit brothers came on the scene. GOB says mum and dad are like Lady and The Tramp. Everyone says I take after The Tramp.

Name this month:
Pookums Snookums
Best moment: *Running off with the crutch that BOG brought back from the hospital.*

RECIPE OF THE WEEK
Roast Lamb with a Pistachio, Apricot & Lemon Crust
Serves 6–8

Prepare 10 mins **Cook** 1½-2 hours

1.8-2kg (4-4lb 7oz) Waitrose New Zealand leg of lamb
  (bone-in)
3 cloves garlic, sliced
1 tbsp olive oil
50g (2oz) LOVE Life Soft Apricots (dried)
50g (2oz) LOVE Life Pistachios
4 tbsp freshly grated Parmigiano Reggiano
Grated zest and juice of ½ lemon
500g tub Waitrose Lamb Gravy
2 x 170g packs Waitrose Sliced Runner Beans, steamed,
  to serve

1. Preheat the oven to 200C/400F/gas 6. Place the lamb in a roasting tin and pierce all over with a small, sharp knife. Insert slivers of garlic into the piercings. Rub the skin with the olive oil and season. Roast in the oven for 30 minutes, then reduce the temperature to 180C/350F/gas 4, for a further hour.

2. While the lamb is cooking, whizz the apricots and pistachios together in a blender or processor until finely chopped. Stir in the cheese, and lemon zest and juice, and season. Remove the lamb from the oven and press the apricot mixture over the surface of the lamb. Baste with the tin juices and return to the oven for 15 minutes until the crust is golden brown.

3. Remove the lamb from the oven and transfer to a warm platter. Leave to rest for 10 minutes. Add the lamb gravy to the tin juices and bring to simmering point on the hob. Slice and serve the lamb with the gravy and steamed runner beans.

Recipe and photograph from Waitrose. More than 5,000 recipes can be found at www.waitrose.com/recipes

THIS WEEK'S TOP TIP
Start an LPA well before it's needed

MONEY

Giving Lasting Power of Attorney (LPA) to someone you trust is a method of ensuring that they will be able to manage your affairs for you, if you become unable to do so. There are two separate LPAs: one for financial affairs and one for health and welfare. The forms are available from the government website www.gov.uk or can be ordered over the phone on 0300 456 0300. Large print versions are available. Be warned: they take a long time to fill in and must then be certified, usually by a solicitor or other professional. Then they need to be sent to the Office of the Public Guardian to be registered (for a fee), which can take two months. It's a slow process, so don't leave it until it's urgent.

ALL THINGS BRIGHT AND BEAUTIFUL
Morels

The morel is one of the easier edible fungi to identify as it has a cap like a sponge or a honeycomb, pitted with holes, and does not have gills like a traditional mushroom. It's unusual in being a spring mushroom – look for it under trees and hedgerows, in gardens and parks. The pitted cap means morels need thorough washing to get rid of grit and insects. Always cook them – raw morels are mildly toxic.

DON'T QUOTE ME, BUT...

'The secret of staying young is to live honestly, eat slowly, and lie about your age'

Lucille Ball

TINY ISLANDS
BY ROYAL GIFT
The island that can never be sold

YNYS GIFFTAN Dwyryd Estuary, nr Talsarnau, Gwynedd
Size: c. 18 acres **Population:** 0

In the early 1700s, Lord Harlech was presented with a tiny isle in the Dwyryd estuary. The island became known as Ynys Gifftan ('Anne's Gift Island') since the hand that bestowed it belonged to Queen Anne. However, Her Royal Highness doesn't seem to have been convinced that it would be wholly appreciated because she added the caveat that it could never be sold. Three centuries later, the island is in the hands of Francis David Ormsby-Gore, 6th Baron Harlech.

For most of those years, Ynys Gifftan has been inhabited by tenant farmers. It's also open to any day-tripping commoners who might care to visit an island that offers views not only of Snowdon but also of Portmeirion, Clough Williams-Ellis' fantasy village.

The walk to Ynys Gifftan, though short, is something of an adventure. A track passing through fields from Talsarnau station leads to a flat sweep of grass shot through with rivulets like the blue veins of a cheese. These must be stepped across, leapt over or worked around to get to the shore.

Ordnance Survey maps baldly state: 'Public Rights of Way to Ynys Gifftan can be dangerous under tidal conditions'. However, the short passage over the sandy estuary to the southern end of the island presents only one difficulty at low tide – a channel right at the start that is rarely completely dry and will need to be paddled or waded across.

A devastating tsunami swept up here in 1927. Having relatively little low ground, Ynys Gifftan was saved from the worst of its wrath, but the village of Talsarnau found itself ripped apart while the railway line along the coast was destroyed. (Happily, the village recovered.) It was the most exciting thing to happen in the estuary until the late 1960s when Patrick McGoohan brought the television series *The Prisoner* to Portmeirion and filmed scenes of sinister Rovers (actually large meteorological balloons) bouncing across the sand to recapture escapees.

The island is a more or less circular hillock, much overgrown nowadays with bramble, gorse and bracken. Time your visit right and you can go for a swim in one of the little lagoons that form just off the southwestern end at every low tide.

The island's small house still stands and indeed was occupied until a decade or so ago. Accounts written by members of the family who lived on Ynys Gifftan for much of the 20th century portray a difficult life spiced with occasional compensations. Surprisingly, they had no boat – the water was never deep enough for long enough to warrant one – so the times at which they could leave and return were determined by the tide. While this proved the perfect excuse for a late arrival at school, it also meant that it was hard to invite friends over. It kept nosy inspectors away during the war (butter remained plentiful on the island for the duration) but could also impede the local doctor in an emergency.

HOW TO GET THERE
It's a half-mile walk from Talsarnau station to the point where you can cross over to the island at low tide. Depending on how much you're prepared to wade (and the tide races in here so you should never go too deep), the island can be accessible up to three hours either side of low tide.

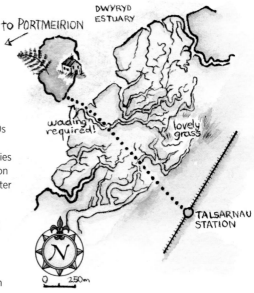

RECIPE OF THE WEEK
Italian Pan-fried Fish with White Bean Purée
Serves 4

Prepare 10 mins **Cook** 15 mins
*2 large essential Waitrose Baking Potatoes,
    peeled and cubed
2 tbsp plain flour
2 tsp Bart Italian Seasoning
4 x 150g (5oz) firm white fish fillets, such as pollack,
    cod or haddock
2-3 tbsp light olive oil
400g can essential Waitrose Cannellini Beans,
    drained and rinsed
25g pack fresh flat-leaf parsley, roughly chopped
1 tsp Dijon mustard
2 x 240g packs tenderstem broccoli spears, cooked,
    to serve*

1. Place the potatoes in a large pan, cover with water, bring to the boil and cook for 12 minutes until almost tender.
2. Meanwhile, mix together the flour and Italian seasoning and dust the fish fillets with the mixture.
3. Heat a little oil in a large non-stick frying pan and cook the fish over a fairly high heat for 3-4 minutes on each side, until golden and crusty.
4. Add the cannellini beans to the potato pan and cook for 2-3 minutes until piping hot, then drain lightly and return to the pan. Add a splash of olive oil and, using a hand-held blender, purée until smooth. Stir in the parsley and mustard.
5. Divide the purée between 4 warmed plates and serve with the fish and broccoli spears.
Recipe and photograph from Waitrose. More than 5,000 recipes can be found at www.waitrose.com/recipes

THIS WEEK'S TOP TIP
Here's a fine thing

BEAUTY
If you have fine hair, watch how you apply conditioner. Avoid rich, heavy formulations as these will make your hair lank; and make sure you use conditioner only on the ends of your hair, not on the scalp. Rethinking your hairstyle can help, too – avoid wispy layers and go for a bob or a blunt cut to make hair look thicker. Adding subtle highlights can also give the impression of volume.

ALL THINGS BRIGHT AND BEAUTIFUL
Slowworms
Slowworms may look like snakes but they're actually legless lizards. If you want proof, look at their eyes. Like lizards, slowworms have eyelids – whereas snakes do not. When the weather warms up, they emerge from hibernation to feed on slugs, snails and small insects. The female gives birth to live babies rather than laying eggs – an advantage in our unpredictable climate as the eggs stay warm and protected in the mother's body.

DON'T QUOTE ME, BUT...
'Age is an issue of mind over matter... if you don't mind, it doesn't matter'
Mark Twain

'Say, "Arrrr!"'

UNEXPECTED ANNIVERSARIES
CHANNEL HOPPER
April 2014 is the 102nd anniversary of:
Harriet Quimby's pioneering solo flight across the English Channel

Harriet Quimby was one of the first female screenwriters, and the first American woman to become a licensed pilot; she used to fly in a distinctive purple outfit, the colour of her sponsors, the Vin Fiz Grape-Soda Company. She was the first woman to fly the English Channel, three years after Bleriot – but barely anyone heard about her record-breaking flight then or since, because she completed it the day after the Titanic sank. The papers weren't interested, so her feat went largely unreported. She died just three months later, at an air show in Massachusetts, after falling from her plane in mid-flight.

WOTEVA!
Teenage translator

Geekstress
A female geek – can be very intimidating to teenage boys, especially if she's attractive

Googleheimer's disease
You want to search for something on Google, but by the time you boot up your computer you have completely forgotten what it was. Who are you again?

Hot mess
Someone who is flustered, dishevelled and maybe short of time, but radiates a certain sensuality

PET OF THE MONTH
Who, me?

Name: Daisy
Owner: Ivo Delingpole
Best habit: Unbridled enthusiasm for my owner
Worst habit: Making friends with all the guests at the local guesthouse
Likes: Hoovering up cat food
Dislikes: Wheelie bins and vacuum cleaners
Personality: Open and outgoing
Naughtiest moment: Digging a bone hole in the newly dug raised beds
Most human trait: Faked innocence

TOP TECHIE TIP
Spammers in the works

Spam is unsolicited junk mail, but it's much more dangerous than the stuff that comes through your letterbox. There are three categories. The first is dubious sales offers; the second is the fake personal appeal to greed; and third are emails that exploit forgetfulness – reminding you of a long-lost bank account and asking you to reply with your account details so they can send over your balance. As if! One word: **don't**. Just delete any dubious or too-good-to-be-true messages. Most email programs contain filters that will weed out spam by spotting key words – obscenities and the like.

JOKE OF THE MONTH
What do you get if you cross an owl with a skunk? A bird that smells but doesn't give a hoot.

sent in by David Haverty

HOW TO MAKE EASTER BIRD DECORATIONS

Easter tables look lovely topped with painted eggs dangling from a blossom branch, but this is a refreshing alternative that allows for greater creativity. It's also simple enough for children to make

YOU WILL NEED
Felt for 1 bird and 3 eggs,
plus scraps for decorating
60cm (24in) length of ribbon or tape
Sequins or anything else you fancy
for decorating the birds and eggs

WHAT TO DO
1. Cut out 2 felt pieces for the bird and 6 egg shapes.
2. Decorate each side of the pieces. Face the birds towards each other on the table to make sure the wings will be attached to the correct side for sewing together later on.
  Sew a wing to the facing side of each bird and embroider an eye with a satin stitch or any simple stitch. When decorating the eggs, we attached and embroidered a simple bird onto one egg, a felt flower shape and a small heart to the second, and sequins to the third. Anything goes, so feel free to add whatever you want.
3. Fold over one end of the ribbon to make a loop and stitch this into place. For added decoration you could sew through a sequin or button to join the loop.
4. Sandwich the ribbon between the two pieces of your first egg, then pin it in place. Sew around the egg with blanket or running stitch.
5. Repeat the above process for each motif, placing them around 9cm (3½in) apart.
6. For the last egg, catch the end of the ribbon and tuck it between the egg pieces.

TIP
You can make your decoration any length and have any number of birds and eggs on it, but make sure you have enough ribbon before you start.

USE IT OR LOSE IT
BRAIN EXERCISE
Give your grey matter a work-out

SUDOKU
The game of logic. Place each of the digits 1 to 9 in each row, column and 3x3 box. There is only one solution.

							8	
	7				6			1
		5		1			9	6
	3	4		6		5		
2								3
		1		2		6	4	
5	9		8		7			
7			3				2	
		3						

GRAMMAR CHALLENGE
The Lynne Truss test Can you spot the errors in grammar, punctuation and spelling? See below for the correct version.

i have another hopeful peak in the fridge as if something might have changed from last time but theres still nothing to eat its a very modern and shameful predicament but it makes me think that an interesting reality tv show could be made perhaps along the lines of how clean is your house experts would come into kitchens like mine and ask how long could you last in a siege that would be an eye opener all the foodstuffs could be laid out and analysed in terms of what you could make and how long youd last in the event of a civil emergency

APRIL'S GENERAL KNOWLEDGE QUIZ

1. The 1933 FA Cup Final on April 29 between Everton and Manchester City was the first in which players wore...
A. Shinpads, B. Hats when they were presented to royalty, C. Shirt numbers, D. Captain's armbands

2. In 1968, which song beat Cliff Richard's *Congratulations* to Eurovision Song Contest glory by 'un point'?
A. Spain's *La La La*, B. Germany's *Hi, Hi, Hi*, C. Malta's *Me, Me, Me*, D. Portugal's *Why, Why, Why*

3. Which actress played April Dancer in *The Girl from UNCLE*?
A. Stefanie Powers, B. Elizabeth Montgomery, C. Dorothy Provine, D. Julie Newmar

4. A patent for which food was issued in the US in April 1896?
A. Muesli, B. Corn Flakes, C. Weetabix, D. Shredded Wheat

5. Which became Britain's first national park in 1951?
A. Exmoor, B. Peak District, C. Lake District, D. New Forest

6. Which musical opened on Broadway in April 1968?
A. *Sweet Charity*, B. *Hair*, C. *A Chorus Line*, D. *Funny Girl*

7. Dudley Moore (b. April 1935) gained a scholarship to Oxford to study what?
A. The organ, B. Astronomy, C. Medicine, D. Greek

8. The 7th and 23rd fence at Aintree is named after which Grand National winner?
A. Red Rum, B. West Tip, C. Foinavon, D. Aldaniti

9. The character Lady Bountiful appears in which Restoration play by Irish dramatist George Farquar (d. April 1707)
A. *The Scornful Lady*, B. *The Recruiting Officer*, C. *The Beaux' Stratagem*, D. *The Constant Couple*

10. *April, Come She Will* is on which Simon & Garfunkel album?
A. *Wednesday Morning 3am*, B. *Sounds of Silence*, C. *Parsley, Sage, Rosemary and Thyme*, D. *Bookends*

I have another, hopeful, peek in the fridge – as if something might have changed from last time. But there's still nothing to eat. It's a very modern – and shameful – predicament, but it makes me think that an interesting reality TV show could be made, perhaps along the lines of *How Clean is Your House?* Experts would come into kitchens such as mine and ask 'How Long Could You Last in a Siege?' That would be an eye-opener. All the foodstuffs could be laid out and analysed in terms of what you could make and how long you'd last in the event of a civil emergency.

5	8	7	2	9	6	3	4	1
6	2	1	5	4	3	8	9	7
4	9	3	7	1	8	2	6	5
8	4	9	6	3	2	7	1	5
3	1	6	8	5	4	7	9	2
2	7	5	9	6	1	4	3	8
9	6	4	1	7	5	8	2	3
1	3	2	5	9	8	6	7	4
7	5	8	4	2	3	9	1	6

ANSWERS
1. C, 2. A,
3. A, 4. B,
5. B, 6. B,
7. A, 8. C,
9. C, 10. B

MAY 2014

SURF'S UP
Saunton Sands, North Devon
Photograph by Saga Magazine
reader Patricia Malek

MAY

1
Thursday

2
Friday

3
Saturday

4
Sunday

5
Monday
Bank Holiday

6
Tuesday

7
Wednesday

8
Thursday

9
Friday

10
Saturday

11
Sunday

12
Monday

13
Tuesday

14
Wednesday

15
Thursday

16
Friday

17
Saturday

18
Sunday

Saga Magazine has everything you need to fill your days

Diary looking a bit empty this month? Pick up your copy of Saga and turn to the Out There pages. Every month we give you details of events all over the country, from music festivals to literary get-togethers, celebratory anniversaries and days out. We review the latest films and give you the lowdown on what everyone's talking about – from plays, musicals and dance, to unmissable exhibitions. And you can find even more online at **www.saga.co.uk/magazine**. To subscribe call 0800 056 1057 or go to **www.saga.co.uk/magazine-subscriptions**

19
Monday

20
Tuesday

Gardening RHS Chelsea Flower Show
Royal Hospital Chelsea, London (to May 24)

21
Wednesday

Art Kenneth Clark: Patron and Pundit
Tate Britain, Millbank, London (to August 10)

22
Thursday

23
Friday

24
Saturday

25
Sunday

26
Monday
Bank Holiday

27
Tuesday

28
Wednesday

29
Thursday

30
Friday

31
Saturday

DECADE BUSTERS

MAY
BIRTHDAYS

TURNING 70
Richard O'Sullivan *actor*
Lynn Barber *journalist*

TURNING 60
Peter Duncan
  (right) TV presenter

TURNING 50
John Parrott
  snooker player
Earl Spencer
  aristocrat

THIS WEEK'S TOP TIP
Grow some strawberry plants
in a container

GARDENING

If you like a handful of strawberries with your muesli in the morning, try planting up a container or a growbag in a sunny spot. Traditionally strawberries are grown from runners, planted in autumn to fruit the next year. But garden centres sell ready-grown plants. Repot them into a suitable container – a growbag will hold six plants, a small window box three, or pot up individually in 20cm (8in) pots. Keep the plants well watered and, once they start to flower, mulch round the base of the plant with straw or black plastic to keep the fruit clean.

Your closest rival will be the blackbirds, which have a canny knack of knowing when the berries are just ripe. Slugs are even worse and will start feasting on underripe berries.

When choosing varieties, as well as researching flavour, note whether plants crop once in June or July or produce fruit on and off into the autumn.

RECIPE OF THE WEEK
Grilled Mackerel & New Potato Salad
Serves 4

Prepare 5 mins **Cook** 30 mins
500g (1lb 2oz) new potatoes such as baby
Jersey Royals, halved
½ cucumber, peeled and cut into large cubes
4 tbsp mayonnaise
1 tbsp wholegrain mustard
2 tbsp lemon juice
4 fresh mackerel, butterflied

1. Cook the potatoes in boiling water for 15-20 minutes until tender. Drain and mix with the cucumber. In a bowl stir together the mayonnaise, wholegrain mustard, half the lemon juice with seasoning and toss with the warm potatoes and cucumber.
2. Preheat the grill to high. Brush the mackerel with the remaining lemon juice and season, then grill for 4-5 minutes on each side until the flesh is firm and flakes easily. Arrange the warm potato and cucumber salad on serving plates and place the mackerel fillets on top.
Recipe and photograph from Waitrose. More than 5,000 recipes can be found at www.waitrose.com/recipes

ALL THINGS BRIGHT AND BEAUTIFUL
Swallows, swifts and martins
After wintering in Africa, swallows, along with swifts, house martins and sand martins, return to the UK to breed every year. After their epic migration, they rear at least two broods *(above)* in a summer. You can distinguish between the species as follows: swallows have a reddish chest; swifts have a distinctive scimitar silhouette; house martins have a white rump; and, unlike the other three, sand martins do not nest in/on houses but in river banks.

DON'T QUOTE ME, BUT...
**'Old age is an excellent time for outrage.
My goal is to say or do at least
one outrageous thing every week'**
Maggie Kuhn

Albums in the attic

Cigarette cards – originally given away free
– are highly collectable, especially those produced
by obscure brands or on arcane subjects

Collecting cigarette cards was a craze among children before the Second World War, which makes one wonder what those young enthusiasts did with their collections after they had grown up. Some may still be in albums on bookshelves but others will have been relegated to the attic long ago.

All the big tobacco companies produced cards on subjects as diverse as butterflies, cricketers, trains and different-shaped noses. If you search hard enough you'll find a card to match almost every subject and, if it's post 1900, there will often be some useful information on the back. WD & HO Wills started the trend in the 1880s and more than 300 other tobacco companies followed suit. Rarity is the key to value: either in terms of a long-forgotten company or an unusual subject.

A set called 'The Life of King Edward V111', for example, was cancelled when he abdicated and is now worth hundreds of pounds.

The golden age of card collecting more or less ended with the outbreak of war. It's difficult now to imagine a children's hobby linked with smoking.

SOLD

The defunct tobacco company Taddy and Co produced very few cards, which explains why someone paid £590 for this trapeze artist at Special Auction Services of Newbury in March 2013

REDISCOVERED BOOK

'This is the forgotten Daphne du Maurier that everyone should read'

The Parasites
Daphne du Maurier
(Virago, £9.99)

Maria, Niall and Celia grew up in the travelling circus of a theatrical family. None of them has quite adapted to life in the real world and they all rely to a certain extent on the willing or unwilling generosity of others. At the opening of the book Maria's infuriated husband erupts, forcing the siblings to consider their lives. Set in 1949 and alternately comic and poignant, this is the forgotten Daphne du Maurier that everyone should read.

As chosen by the staff of Slightly Foxed bookshop, specialists in unusual titles, old and new; www.foxedbooks.com

'Can I borrow your hedge trimmers?'

THIS WEEK'S TOP TIP

Look after your teeth and you'll be taking care of your general health too

HEALTH

If you don't clean your teeth properly it can have a knock-on effect. Poor oral hygiene can lead to inflammation of the mouth, which in turn increases your risk of stroke, heart disease, lung disease and even type 2 diabetes. These days, rechargeable electric toothbrushes and sonic versions make cleaning teeth so much easier – and more effective.

Flossing is also recommended to keep gum disease at bay. If you find this tricky, it might be worth investing in one of the latest electric water flossers. Your dentist or hygienist will have all the latest information.

RECIPE OF THE WEEK
Asparagus & Goat's Cheese Tart
Serves 6

Prepare 15 mins **Cook** 50 mins

1 x 230g sheet Waitrose Cooks' Ingredients Shortcrust Pastry, thawed
230g (8oz) bunch English asparagus, trimmed
130g pack Butlers Ravens Oak goat's cheese, cubed
4 medium free-range eggs
150ml (¼ pint) single cream
½ x 15g pack chives, snipped

1. Preheat the oven to 200C/400F/gas 6. Unroll the pastry sheet and line a 23cm (9in) loose-bottomed flan tin with it, trimming the excess to fit. Prick with a fork. Chill in the fridge for 10 minutes, then line with a crumpled sheet of greaseproof paper over the pastry and weigh it down with baking beans or rice grains. Bake blind for 10 minutes, then remove the beans or rice and paper and return to the oven for a further 5 minutes.
2. Meanwhile, steam the asparagus for 4-5 minutes until just tender. Drain and run under cold water. Pat dry with kitchen paper and cut into 5cm (2in) lengths. Arrange over the base of the pastry case and scatter with the cubed goat's cheese.
3. Whisk together the eggs, cream and chives. Season the mixture and pour into the pastry case. Bake for 30-35 minutes until the filling is set and the top golden. Serve warm or cold with a salad.
Recipe and photograph from Waitrose. More than 5,000 recipes can be found at www.waitrose.com/recipes

ALL THINGS BRIGHT AND BEAUTIFUL
May blossom
Hawthorn or may blossom is garlanded with superstition. 'Cast ne'er a clout 'ere may is out' was a phrase often heard in the Fifties when children were keen to discard woolly winter vests. And most regional folklore is emphatically against bringing branches of may into the house – whether for its papist associations after the Reformation or simply because the flowers smell of decay. (Their scent is based on triethylamine, a chemical produced when flesh rots.)

DON'T QUOTE ME, BUT...
'I've found the best way to give advice to your children is to find out what they want, then advise them to do it'
Harry Truman

MAY
DRINK OF THE MONTH

MOJITO

Bright green leaves – just
the thing for spring

8 mint leaves
Half a lime, chopped
15ml (½fl oz) sugar syrup
Ice cubes
60ml (2fl oz) white rum
Soda water

Muddle the mint and lime with the
sugar syrup in a cocktail shaker.
Add a scoop of ice, then the rum.
Shake vigorously and strain into
a chilled tumbler up to about
2.5cm (1 in) from the top, then top
up with soda water.

BADGER'S BLOG

'I'VE NEVER BEEN SO INSULTED IN ALL MY LIFE'

Badger lets her owners know exactly what she thinks
about substandard merchandise

There are three special days
every year. Valentine's, my
birthday, and Christmas. This
month it's my birthday and I usually
expect something pretty special from
the DFLs. In the past they haven't
done badly. We once went to a dog-
friendly hotel in the West Country
(why aren't they all dog-friendly?). On
another occasion they invited Geoff
to stay – he's an Australian 'kelpie'
and the most terrifying-looking dog
I've ever seen, like a cross between
a wolf and a dingo. But he turned out
to be the gentlest dog EVER; then
they invited some cousins down
with five different dogs, including Tess
the retired greyhound. Now, she
really was terrifying and made it very
clear who was in charge. Talk about
Alpha females – I willingly rolled over
and downgraded to Zeta the moment
she arrived.

You might see a pattern emerging
here: dogs. I love the company of
other dogs (especially Wilf). So you
can probably imagine that I wasn't
overjoyed when one year for my
birthday they got me a cheap dog
basket with no other dog in sight. It
wouldn't have been quite so bad if it
hadn't still had the name of the shop
and the price attached. 'Tricky Trev's,
£9.99'. Now I'm no Mary Portas, but
even I know that Tricky Trev's is not
exactly Harrods or Fortnums. I've
never been so insulted in all my life.

So I showed them what I thought
and made pretty short work of it.
That'll teach them to fob me off with
anything less than a top-of-the-range
basket. Not that I'd ever sleep in it,
when there are perfectly good sofas
available, but it's the principle.

I think they must have realised how
upset I was because we went
to my favourite wood every day for
a week. And it's bluebell time at
the moment, which is even more
reason to go. BOG assured me
that 'when my time came' he would
make sure I'd be here every day for
ever and ever. I'm not quite sure what
he meant, but I like the sound of it!

Name this month: *Boofuls*
Best moment: *Total destruction of an
unsuitable dog basket*

THIS WEEK'S TOP TIP
Is your driving licence up to date?

MONEY

Failure to renew your photo licence carries a hefty fine if you're driving around after it's expired – much better to pay the small fee to get it renewed. You can renew online at www.gov.uk or at the post office. If you've still got an old paper licence – ie if you've never had to register a change of address and been issued with a photocard as a result – it will be valid until you're 70. Renewals after age 70 are free of charge.

ALL THINGS BRIGHT AND BEAUTIFUL
Bluebells

Bluebells grow in woods right across the UK, from Scotland to Cornwall. The easiest way to tell a true bluebell from a Spanish interloper (a garden escapee) is to look at the way the flowers hang from the stem: native bluebells have stems that curve over at the top so that the bells hang down on one side of the stem; Spanish bluebells have stouter, more upright stems with flowers all around.

The two species can hybridise however, so you can get a combination of characteristics from both plants.

DON'T QUOTE ME, BUT...
'Youth is when you're allowed to stay up late on New Year's Eve. Middle age is when you're forced to'
Bill Vaughan

RECIPE OF THE WEEK
Crunchy Chicken with Griddled Courgette & Feta Salad
Serves 4

Prepare 20 mins **Cook** 20 mins
2 tbsp plain flour
1 egg, beaten
100g (4oz) Tuc Original Biscuits, crushed to fine crumbs
4 chicken breast fillets
2 tbsp olive oil
Small knob butter
For the courgette & feta salad:
3 medium courgettes, finely sliced lengthways on a vegetable peeler
2 tbsp extra-virgin olive oil
Grated zest and juice of ½ lemon
Small handful fresh mint or basil, finely chopped
75g (3oz) feta, crumbled

1. Place the flour, beaten egg and Tuc biscuits in three separate shallow bowls. Roll the chicken breasts in the flour, shake off the excess and then dip in the egg and finally in the biscuit crumbs.
2. Heat the olive oil and butter in a large frying pan over a gentle heat; add the chicken and cook for 6-7 minutes. Turn over and cook for another 6-7 minutes or until golden brown on both sides and cooked through. Remove from the heat and set aside.
3. Meanwhile, preheat a griddle pan until hot. Brush the courgette slices with a little oil, season and then griddle in batches until tender and charred. Repeat until all the slices have been griddled.
4. Transfer the courgettes to a serving bowl. Squeeze over a little lemon juice and a grating of lemon zest, then scatter with the herbs and crumbled feta and serve with the hot crunchy chicken.
Recipe and photograph from Waitrose. More than 5,000 recipes can be found at www.waitrose.com/recipes

TINY ISLANDS
SPLIT ASUNDER

The Isle of May has taken a pounding
from the waves

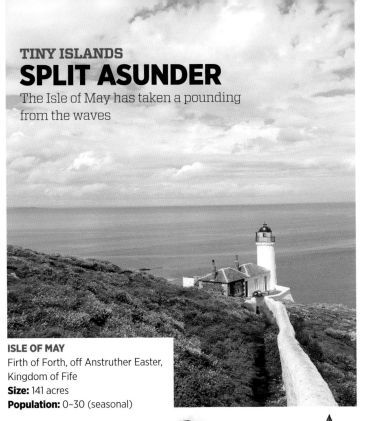

ISLE OF MAY

Firth of Forth, off Anstruther Easter,
Kingdom of Fife

Size: 141 acres

Population: 0–30 (seasonal)

Spend five minutes on the Isle of May and any questions you may have had as to why it was recognised as a National Nature Reserve as long ago as 1956 are blown away in a gale of flapping wings. From the moment arctic terns greet you with anguished cries and sharp bills as you walk up from the little harbour at Kirkhaven, there's simply no getting away from the natural world.

A staggering quarter of a million seabirds breed here each year, of which 90,000 or so are puffins, the very best creature that ever flew over the Earth. Of course, that's not to belittle the shags, eiders, kittiwakes, guillemots, razorbills, fulmars and the dive-bombing arctic terns, whose cousins the sandwich and common tern also make an appearance. In fact, an astonishing 250 species of birds have been spotted here, including unexpected visitors such as owls, woodpeckers and nightingales.

A little up from the harbour stand the scant ruins of a 12th-century monastery dedicated to St Ethernan, as well as traces of earlier remains of religious buildings on the same site.

May was almost certainly a place of spiritual significance long before a Christian missionary called Monanus (later St Monanus, naturally) arrived around AD840, probably as one of a group led by St Ethernan all the way from Hungary. However, in 875 he and all the new converts (about 6,000 men, women and children) were slaughtered on the East Neuk mainland by the men of the Danish King Humber. A small band of Christians including Ethernan escaped to May but the Vikings tracked them down and murdered them on 4 March (St Ethernan's Day). Half of the saint's stone coffin later floated miraculously across to the mainland, where it can be seen to this day in Anstruther Wester churchyard. The island's status as a focus for Christian pilgrimage was duly sealed.

Fluke Street is May's main drag, where most of today's inhabitants live. The unappealing utilitarian buildings lead to a man-made freshwater loch. Above is the main lighthouse, up a sharpish incline jokingly nicknamed 'Palpitation Brae' for its ability to get hearts pounding violently when climbed.

The island has been all but split into four by the grinding and gnashing of the waves. To reach the far north-western portions of the island – Rona and North Ness – a bridge is necessary (and has collapsed, so that bit of May is off limits until it's repaired).

May was home to Scotland's very first manned 'light beacon' way back in 1636 – a beautiful three-storey square tower with a beacon on top fired by coal lifted by a pulley. The fact that the ground floor is still here is thanks to Sir Walter Scott, who suggested that the newly obsolete structure should not be pulled down as planned but 'ruined à la picturesque'.

While the beacon doubtless saved many lives in its 180 years, it was also the scene of tragedy. For two nights in January 1791 sailors noticed that there was no light coming from May. They discovered seven members of the Anderson family, keepers of the light, had perished while they slept due to carbon monoxide and sulphur dioxide blowing in from smouldering ashes. Only an infant survived, though quite how is not known.

HOW TO GET THERE

The Isle of May is open to the public from April to September. Either take the train to North Berwick and then a Seafari RIB from the Scottish Seabird Centre for about 2.5 hours on the island. Or take the train to Markinch, the 43A bus to Leven, then the no 95 to Anstruther to board either the Anstruther Pleasure Cruises' May Princess, or the Osprey of Anstruther's speedier RIB. Both offer two to three hours on the island.

RECIPE OF THE WEEK
Banoffee Cake with Caramel, Chocolate & Banana
Makes 12 slices

Prepare 15 mins **Cook** 1 hour

75g (3oz) butter, softened
25g (1oz) caster sugar
1 large free-range egg
397g can Nestlé Carnation Caramel
225g (8oz) plain flour
2 tsp baking powder
3 ripe bananas, mashed
50g (2oz) Waitrose Cooks' Ingredients Dark Chocolate
  Chunks

1. Preheat the oven to 180C/350F/gas 4. Grease and base-line a 1kg (2lb) loaf tin.
2. Beat the butter and sugar together until pale and fluffy, then add the egg, followed by the caramel. Mix the flour and the baking powder together and gradually fold into the caramel mixture.
3. Fold in the mashed bananas and ¾ of the chocolate chunks and pour into the prepared tin. Sprinkle with the remaining chocolate.
4. Bake for 1 hour, covering loosely with foil for the last 15 minutes if it gets too dark. A skewer inserted in the centre should come out clean.
5. Allow the cake to cool slightly before removing from the tin and slicing.
Recipe and photograph from Waitrose. More than 5,000 recipes can be found at www.waitrose.com/recipes

THIS WEEK'S TOP TIP
Emergency eye masks

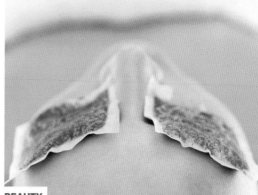

BEAUTY

Overindulging in alcohol can cause fluid retention, which may result in puffiness around the eyes. Don't try to cover up with make-up: you'll make things look worse. Instead try a ten-minute emergency eye mask. If you've got one, use a cooling gel mask or eye pads (kept on standby in the fridge); otherwise make do with slices of cucumber or cooled tea bags. Leave in place for ten minutes.

ALL THINGS BRIGHT AND BEAUTIFUL
Bats

Bats use echo-location to detect insect prey but some moths have evolved to take evasive action when they hear the sounds. The brown long-eared bat has gone a step further and developed a very quiet echo-location system. To detect the signals that bounce back it has huge ears – nearly three-quarters of the length of the head and body – that act as parabolic reflectors to concentrate the sound.

DON'T QUOTE ME, BUT...
'You can't help getting older, but you don't have to get old'
George Burns

President Kennedy's
Birthday Party
MAY 19, 1962
MADISON SQUARE GARDEN
GALA ALL STAR SHOW
END ARENA
SEC   ROW   SEAT
112   O
CONTRIBUTION $10. PER PERSON
New York's Birthday Salute To The President, Inc.
SPONSORED BY THE STATE AND NATIONAL DEMOCRATIC
COMMITTEES AND CITIZENS FOR KENNEDY

PRESIDENT KENNEDY'S
BIRTHDAY PARTY
•
SATURDAY EVENING
MAY 19, 1962
MADISON SQUARE GARDEN
8:30 P. M.
END ARENA
SEC   ROW   SEAT
112   O
CONTRIBUTION
$10.
PER PERSON

UNEXPECTED ANNIVERSARIES
HAPPY BIRTHDAY, MR PRESIDENT

May 19, 2014 is the 52nd anniversary of:

Marilyn Monroe's show-stopping performance

John F Kennedy's celebratory bash was held at Madison Square Garden ten days before his 45th birthday – it was neatly combined with a fundraising event for the Democrats and more than 15,000 people paid to attend *(see ticket above)*. In retrospect the event has an added poignancy as it was one of Marilyn's last performances – she died later that summer on August 5 at home in Los Angeles. She was just 36 years old.

Her dress has become as famous as the sultry version of the song – flesh-toned, studded with rhinestones and so tight that she really was sewn into it. It sold at auction in New York in 1999 for more than a million dollars – a fitting sum, since that's exactly how it made her look.

'How do you like your toast?'

WOTEVA!
Teenage translator

Bare Gutteridge
Not just something that is bad, not even something that is really bad, but something that is really, REALLY bad. Like double maths, or something

LOL
Laughing out loud. Caution: if a teen says 'lol' in conversation, rather than actually laughing, they have left our world and moved into that fourth dimension known as smartphone space

Toothpaste hangover
Everything tastes awful after you've just brushed your teeth. Ever noticed that?

The brothers

Names: Frisky, Digger, Ginger and Nippy
Owner's name: Louise Bowen
Best habits: Snuggling up together and looking sweet
Worst habits: Fighting each other
Like: Hand-fed pumpkin seeds
Dislike: Being held or played with
Personality: Permanently industrious
Naughtiest moment: Colluding on an escape plan for Frisky, which worked. A week living under the dishwasher ensued
Most human trait: Dozing off lying on their backs, feet in air

---

Instagram in an instant

Instagram is a social network and smartphone app where updates are made using photos instead of text. Linking Instagram to other social networks is simple and lets you share your photos via social media. So how do you use it? First off, you'll need the right phone: an iPhone or an Android. Once the free app is installed, create an account and you can start uploading photos. Instagram has a great selection of filters, including sepia, and black and white, for instant retro appeal.

'Doctor, Doctor, I think I'm going deaf.'
'Hmm, what are the symptoms?'
'Well, Homer's a fat, lazy bloke, and Marge has got blue hair.'

sent in by Terry Mills

HOW TO MAKE SUMMER BUNTING

Strung from leafy branches and blowing gently in a warm breeze, fabric bunting brings a festive air to the summer garden. Good times are here, it seems to say, suggesting parties, and wholesome fun and games

WHAT YOU'LL NEED

A mixture of plain, striped and floral cotton fabrics (fabric scraps or swatches need to be at least 22cm/ 8½in square)
16m (17½yd) coloured tape or binding, a minimum of 2cm (¾in) wide
Cotton thread for machine sewing

WHAT TO DO

1. Using pinking shears (so that you don't have to hem each piece), cut out 50 triangles, each measuring 22cm (8½in) wide and deep. Decide on the order of your triangles, aiming to get a good mix of patterns and colours.
2. Fold the tape in half lengthways and iron it in place to make a long channel for inserting the triangles.
3. Starting about 20cm (8in) in from the end of the tape (to leave some free for tying), pin the triangles in position, 10cm (4in) apart, opening up the tape and slipping the top of each triangle inside so the raw edge is hidden. Stop 20cm (8in) short of the other end of the tape.
4. Machine carefully into place all along the length of the tape, to secure the triangles.
5. Making a loop at either end can make hanging easier. Extra tape can also be added to extend the bunting or to make it easier to tie on to trees and so on.

TIPS

Bunting looks beautiful indoors as well as out, looped along verandahs, draped across doorways or hung in swags around the walls of a child's bedroom all year round. This bunting will be machine-washable and is best kept folded flat in a box between uses to prevent it getting tangled.

BRAIN EXERCISE

Give your grey matter a work-out

SUDOKU

The game of logic. Place each of the digits 1 to 9 in each row, column and 3x3 box. There is only one solution.

		5			6			
1	4			8		2		
		9				5	8	
2	3	4			5	1		
	5	8		2		9	6	
3	4			7				
7		8			4	6		
	9			3				

GRAMMAR CHALLENGE

The Lynne Truss test Can you spot the errors in grammar, punctuation and spelling? See below for the correct version.

during that week i cleaned well over 100 pears of shoes at a shilling a time was i exhausted of course not you pathetic worm you dont get exhausted at that age the next year my bob a job money making scheme was to get a second hand pram wheel it to the station and ferry passengers luggage to their holiday hotels on the seafront that failed hopelessly because when i wasnt looking the taxi drivers i was doing out of business sabotaged my pram by taking the wheels off i never appreciated then that this knack i had for making money was something special

During that week I cleaned well over 100 pairs of shoes at a shilling a time. Was I exhausted? Of course not, you pathetic worm! You don't get exhausted at that age. The next year, my Bob-a-Job money-making scheme was to get a second-hand pram, wheel it to the station and ferry passengers' luggage to their holiday hotels on the seafront. That failed hopelessly because, when I wasn't looking, the taxi-drivers I was doing out of business sabotaged my pram by taking the wheels off. I never appreciated at the time that this knack I had for making money was something special.

MAY'S GENERAL KNOWLEDGE QUIZ

1. Who did Henry VIII marry in May, 1536?
A. Catherine Parr, B. Catherine of Aragon,
C. Jane Seymour, D. Anne of Cleves

2. Grace Jones plays villainess May Day in which James Bond film?
A. *View to a Kill*, B. *For Your Eyes Only*,
C. *Octopussy*, D. *The Living Daylights*

3. What's the name of the popular English May Day celebrations figure?
A. Michael of May, B. Jack in the Green,
C. Jack O'Roses, D. St Stephen with a rose

4. Who stood for the Conservatives in Clwyd South in the May 1997 General Election?
A. George Osborne, B. Michael Gove,
C. Boris Johnson, D. Theresa May

5. Singer Donovan celebrates his 67th birthday on May 10. What is his surname?
A. Kyle, B. Mackay. C. Scott, D. Leitch

6. Who did actress Elizabeth Taylor marry in May 1959?
A. Eddie Fisher, B. Michael Wilding,
C. Conrad Hilton, D. Michael Todd

7. Who described maypoles as 'a Heathenish vanity'?
A. The 1644 Long Parliament, B. Vincent Price in the film *Witchfinder General*, C. Mary Whitehouse, D. Dr Ian Paisley

8. In *Treasure Island*, published in May 1883, what was the name of the inn run by Jim Hawkins' mother?
A. The Spyglass, B. The Hispaniola,
C. The Admiral Benbow, D. The Captain Flint

9. Towel Day on May 25 commemorates the death of which British comedy writer?
A. Douglas Adams, B. Michael Flanders,
C. Eddie Braben, D. Graham Chapman

10. Which English eastern coastal town is featured in *Dracula*, first published in May 1897?
A. Cleethorpes, B. Scarborough, C. Whitby, D. Lowestoft

ANSWERS
1. C, 2. A,
3. B, 4. C,
5. D, 6. A,
7. A, 8. C,
9. A, 10. C

8	9	6	1	4	3	2	7	5
1	7	2	8	6	5	4	9	3
3	4	5	2	9	7	6	8	1
4	5	8	7	1	2	3	6	9
7	1	9	3	5	6	8	4	2
2	6	3	9	8	4	5	1	7
6	3	1	5	7	9	4	5	8
5	1	4	6	3	8	7	2	9
9	8	7	5	2	1	6	3	4

TRAVEL
MONEMVASIA

Monemvasia was once a prestigious port of call for ships sailing between Constantinople and Italy, offering a fine resting place for emperors and sultans. Today, it's a fascinating off-the-beaten-track holiday destination in its own right

FIVE Q&AS

Where is Monemvasia? Greece. It's a medieval walled town, almost an island, on a small peninsula off the east coast of the Southern Peloponnese and about 55 miles east of Sparta.

How's the weather? Temperatures can reach 40C in July and August, so it is best to visit from October to April. Springtime is beautiful as wildflowers cover the rocky outcrops.

What's the history? Have you got a week? Monemvasia was part of mainland Greece until it was cut off by an earthquake in 375AD. Since 583AD the town and natural rock fortress has seen Byzantine, Ottoman and Venetian rule. It remained part of the Byzantine Empire until the fall of Constantinople, when it was sold by the Sultan of the Ottoman Empire to Pope Pius II in 1460.

It was one of the most important ports in Greece and 'exchanged hands' between Venetians and Ottomans until 1821, when it was liberated during the Greek War of Independence.

There was more drama during the Second World War, when thousands of New Zealand 6 Brigade soldiers were evacuated from the peninsula in April 1941. They made their getaway before the German Army claimed the town as a refuge for wounded soldiers.

Since 1967, Athenian couple Alexandros and Haris Kalligas have been responsible for restoring more than half of the 160 ancient properties that stand on the rock and their work has earned them a Europa Nostra cultural heritage medal.

Any bright lights? Not really: it's more a place for walking, absorbing history, painting or taking photographs. At night the town lights twinkle on the hillside and there are plenty of small tavernas where you can tuck into fried fish and ouzo.

Catch your breath and take in the view of the Aegean. On a clear day, you can see Crete

Step back in time
No cars are allowed in the old town of Monemvasia

How can I get there? It's a five to six hour drive from Athens. No cars can be driven into the old town: the clue is in the name: *mone* and *emvasia* translate as 'single entrance'. You enter through a narrow arch after making your way up a 200-metre causeway from the harbour.

FOUR THINGS TO KNOW

The sweet dessert wine Malmsey, made from the Malavasia grape, originated in Monemvasia. During 15th-century Venetian rule, large quantities were exported to the UK.

The life of St John the Neomartyr of Monemvasia is celebrated on October 21. The son of a priest, he refused to change his religious beliefs when he was captured by invaders and died from a stab to the heart in 1773.

There are no chain hotels, so all accommodation is unique. You can even stay in the restored castle.

The bridge that connects the mainland to Monemvasia wasn't built until 1971.

THREE THINGS TO REMEMBER

Walking shoes are a must. The higher you walk, the more uneven the paths and steps become. Monemvasia isn't known as the Gibraltar of the East for nothing!

There are plenty of good beaches. Kakavos beach is close by so you can hire a sunbed and have a swim after all that walking. On the other side of the bay it is rocky – but ideal for diving and fishing. Pori beach has shade under the pine trees if you want to avoid too much sun.

July 23 is Monemvasia's Independence Day. Fishing boats fill the harbour, lanes are dressed with bunting and a firework display rounds off the celebrations.

MONEMVASIA, GREECE
LAT. 37°N
LONG. 23°E

A Byzantine church (*above*) and 12th-century Ayia Sophia (*below*)

TWO PLACES TO VISIT

Christos Elkomenos church in the old town is small but perfect and shows Venetian influence. Opposite is Agios Petros, once a church, then a mosque, now a tiny, colourful museum.

In the lower new town, watch fishing boats come in to the pretty harbour. Then later on you can choose the catch of the day at any of the waterside cafés. It's a lovely spot to relax and enjoy the sunshine if walking up to the old town seems too strenuous. Why not order *kourabiedes* as a sweet treat? These rich biscuits are made from almonds or walnuts, dusted with icing sugar and served with coffee or tea. You'll also find a cashpoint here.

ONE MUST-DO

Zigzag your way to the summit. It may be strenuous but the crown jewel is the 12th-century octagonal church of Ayia Sophia, perched on the cliff. From here, catch your breath, and take in the views of the Aegean. On a clear day, you can see Crete.

Does Saga go there?
Yes, find out more about travel to Greece at saga.co.uk/greece

JUNE2014

RETURN OF THE NATIVE POPPY
Field at Chartham, Kent
Photograph by Saga Magazine
reader Therese Allen

JUNE

1
Sunday

2
Monday

3
Tuesday

4
Wednesday

5
Thursday

6
Friday

7
Saturday
The Derby, Epsom

8
Sunday

9
Monday

10
Tuesday
(e/vent) **Art British Folk Art**
Tate Britain, Millbank, London (to Sept 7)

11
Wednesday

12
Thursday

13
Friday

14
Saturday

15
Sunday
Father's Day

16
Monday

17
Tuesday

18
Wednesday

Saga Magazine has everything you need to fill your days

Diary looking a bit empty this month? Pick up your copy of Saga and turn to the Out There pages.
Every month we give you details of events all over the country, from music festivals to literary
get-togethers, celebratory anniversaries and days out. We review the latest films and give you the lowdown
on what everyone's talking about – from plays, musicals and dance, to unmissable exhibitions.
And you can find even more online at **www.saga.co.uk/magazine**. To subscribe call 0800 056 1057
or go to **www.saga.co.uk/magazine-subscriptions**

19
Thursday

20
Friday

21
Saturday

22
Sunday

23
Monday
Wimbledon begins

24
Tuesday

25
Wednesday

26
Thursday

27
Friday

28
Saturday

29
Sunday

30
Monday

DECADE BUSTERS

JUNE
BIRTHDAYS

TURNING 70
Robert Powell *actor*
Ray Davies *singer/
songwriter (The Kinks)*

TURNING 60
Anne Kirkbride *soap actress*

TURNING 50
Boris Johnson
*(right) politician
and journalist*
Kathy Burke *actress*

REX

THIS WEEK'S TOP TIP
Prune spring-flowering shrubs

GARDENING

To get the best performance from spring-flowering shrubs, you need to think ahead. Bushes such as forsythia *(above)*, flowering currant, weigela, philadelphus and winter jasmine all produce blooms on stems they made the previous year.

To boost flowering next spring, cut off all this year's flowering stems, trimming them back to where you can see fresh new growth or fat buds about to burst into leaf. This job is made much easier if you tackle it the minute the shrub has finished flowering.

At the same time, on well-established bushes, it's a good idea to cut out 10-20% of older stems, cutting them off close to the base of the bush. This encourages new strong growth, so that the shrub constantly renews itself. When done, give the shrubs a scattering of fertiliser or mulch with well-rotted manure.

RECIPE OF THE WEEK
Heart-healthy Trout & Dill Fishcakes
Serves 4

Prepare 10 mins + chilling **Cook** 20 mins
280g pack 2 Scottish trout fillets
400g essential Waitrose Mashed Potato
5 salad onions, finely chopped
2 tbsp capers, rinsed and roughly chopped
35g (1½oz) cornichons, finely chopped
½ x 20g pack dill, snipped
2 lemons, 1 zested and juiced, the other in wedges
1 tbsp olive oil
220g (8oz) essential Waitrose Round Beans and 150g (5oz)
*   essential Waitrose Baby Broad Beans, steamed, to serve*

1. Preheat the grill to medium-high. Place the trout on a foil-lined baking tray and grill for 8 minutes. Set aside to cool, then thickly flake, discarding the skin.
2. In a large bowl, mix the mashed potato with the salad onions, capers, cornichons, dill, lemon zest and 2 tbsp juice. Fold through the trout, shape into 8 cakes and chill in the fridge for 15 minutes.
3. Heat the oil in a non-stick pan over a medium heat. Gently cook the fishcakes in 2 batches for 4-5 minutes on each side until golden brown and warmed through.
4. Serve the fishcakes with the steamed vegetables and lemon wedges.
Recipe and photograph from Waitrose. More than 5,000 recipes can be found at www.waitrose.com/recipes

ALL THINGS BRIGHT AND BEAUTIFUL
Nightingales
Nightingales arrive in spring from Africa. The birds are robin-sized and brown. Males sing to establish their territory and attract females – and not just at night. They are mainly found in the south east – below a line between the Humber and the Severn – and generally sing (and nest) in dense scrubby undergrowth, making them nearly impossible to spot. But that song is unmistakable.

DON'T QUOTE ME, BUT...
'Wrinkles should merely indicate where smiles have been'
Mark Twain

REDISCOVERED BOOK

'Life should be perfect, but somehow it isn't quite'

One Fine Day
Mollie Panter-Downes
(Virago, £9.99)

The Second World War is over and life should be perfect, but somehow it isn't quite. The members of the Marshall family are adapting to their new circumstances and this book takes one summer's day in their lives. Strait-laced Stephen almost breaks free of his rigid ways, ten-year-old Victoria longs for the freedom of life on a farm and bohemian Laura, wife and mother, perhaps copes best, floating through the day in a completely charming and captivating way.

As chosen by the staff of Slightly Foxed bookshop, specialists in unusual titles, old and new; www.foxedbooks.com

HIDDEN TREASURES
Watch what you're doing

If you've got a Swiss-made wristwatch – or even just a humble vintage Timex – it's time to get it valued. Here's our history of the timepiece on a bracelet

The wristwatch industry has a curious relationship with conflict. Before the First World War they were made almost exclusively for women. It seems men felt uncomfortable wearing anything resembling a bracelet. But in the trenches, having a timepiece on your wrist was more practical than having one in your pocket, and from the 1920s onwards the industry boomed.

In the Second World War, many watch factories switched to armaments – except for neutral Switzerland, which cornered even more of the market. As a result many of the most collectable watches are Swiss – with brands such as Rolex, Omega, Longines and Patek Philippe to the fore.

Generations past might have abandoned a watch if it stopped working or fashions changed. But now even watches in need of repair might be worth hundreds – provided they have the right pedigree. In contrast to the early 1900s, many fashion-conscious men of today are prepared to spend a fortune on an eye-catching wristwatch. Although Swiss brands dominate, even an old Timex might be worth having checked out. They were able to 'take a licking and keep on ticking' – or so the advertising slogan said.

SOLD

Patek Philippe is the prince of Swiss watch makers and this pink gold example fetched £1,707,104 at Christie's in Geneva in May, 2012

'Bison indeed! You're always exaggerating – they were gerbils!'

IAN BAKER..

THIS WEEK'S TOP TIP
Berries are good for you

HEALTH

Serving up a handful of blueberries and strawberries a couple of times a week can help to keep your mental faculties in tip-top condition.

A recent study from the US suggests that cognitive ageing can be delayed by up to two and a half years in people over 60 by doing just that. The reason is thought to be due to the berries' high quantities of flavonoids, which have powerful antioxidant and anti-inflammatory properties that combat the stress and inflammation associated with cognitive decline. It's a simple addition to make to your diet – for some considerable benefit.

RECIPE OF THE WEEK
Caramel Apple Cake
Serves 10

Prepare 20 mins **Cook** 1 hour
125g (4½oz) unsalted butter, softened, plus extra for buttering
397g can Carnation Caramel
2 medium free-range eggs
225g (8oz) self-raising flour, sifted
2 tsp baking powder
2 tsp ground cinnamon
300g (11oz) Bramley apples, peeled, cored and diced
2 tbsp essential Waitrose Semi-skimmed Milk
1 tbsp demerara sugar

1. Preheat the oven to 150C/300F/gas 3. Place the butter with 225g (8oz) of the caramel in a large bowl and beat with an electric whisk until well combined. Then beat in the eggs one at a time.
2. Sift over the flour, baking powder and cinnamon. Fold together, then gently stir in the apple and the milk.
3. Lightly butter and base-line a 20cm (8in) spring-form cake tin. Spoon in the cake mix, smooth the top and scatter with the demerara sugar. Bake for 1 hour, or until risen and lightly golden on top.
4. Remove the cake from the tin and place on a serving plate. Warm the rest of the caramel in a small saucepan over a low heat until pourable, then drizzle over the top of the cake. Serve, cut into wedges, with a dollop of whipped cream or a scoop of ice cream — or simply with a cup of tea.
Recipe and photograph from Waitrose. More than 5,000 recipes can be found at www.waitrose.com/recipes

ALL THINGS BRIGHT AND BEAUTIFUL
Tadpoles
February's frogspawn gave rise to a thick soup of tadpoles, little more than a mouth, gills and a tail. Now those tadpoles have lost their gills and developed teeth, and grown first back, then front legs. The last stage before a tadpole metamorphoses into a frog is the absorption of the tail. Then the tiny froglet leaves the water and won't return to it for three years, when it is ready to breed.

DON'T QUOTE ME, BUT...
'An archaeologist is the best husband a woman can have. The older she gets, the more interested he is in her'
Agatha Christie

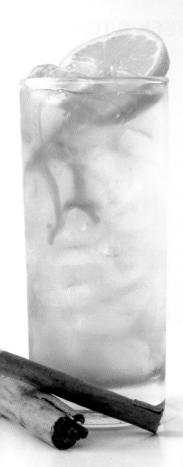

BADGER'S BLOG

'WE RAN AROUND AND REFUSED TO POSE'

Badger won't play ball for the photographer
who's trying to take her portrait

BOG's birthday is in the **month after mine**, which is clearly not as important as mine, but we have to go through the motions anyway. This year GOB had a great idea for his present, which involved me in a starring role. Naturally this appealed to me. Attention is attention, after all.

I couldn't believe my luck when I discovered what she had planned. In fact it was almost good enough to be my own present (but then nothing beats a five-mile walk with some other dogs, followed by a marrow bone and a good long snooze). So when she said that we were going to meet my dog parents for a portrait I was beside myself with excitement. Of course I see Sandy, my very posh pedigree Labrador mum, about the village quite often, but I don't see as much of my dad Ollie – mostly because he's so busy being out on the razzle again.

But here's the best bit: she organised a photographer to do the photos, and agreed the cost with him in advance. He'd never worked with animals before and later said it was the most difficult assignment he'd ever had. Well, we had to make sure we got our money's worth, so we all ran round and round the farmyard all morning and refused to pose and he was there for a lot longer than he'd bargained for.

BOG went silent when he opened his present. He often does this when a) he's happy about something, or b) he doesn't know what to say, or c) he doesn't know what he's looking at. I reckon it was a mixture of all three. He's easily confused. What more could a dog owner want than a picture of his faithful hound with her proud parents? It now has pride of place in his office so he can look at me whenever he's working.

Name this month:
Woofington WooWoos
Best moment: *Spoiling the photographer's day*

RECIPE OF THE WEEK
Simple Salmon & Watercress Tart
Serves 4

Prepare 15 mins **Cook** 50 mins
320g pack ready-rolled all-butter shortcrust pastry
1 leek, finely sliced
2 medium Columbian Blacktail free-range eggs, lightly beaten
150ml (¼ pint) essential Waitrose Whole Milk
30g (1oz) essential Waitrose Grated Parmigiano Reggiano
30g (1oz) watercress leaves (stalks discarded), finely chopped
170g pack Waitrose Lemon & Herb Poached Scottish Salmon Fillets, skin removed
Green salad, to serve

1. Put a baking sheet in the oven and preheat to 200C/400F/gas 6. Line a 20cm (8in) loose-bottomed tart tin with the pastry, prick the bottom with a fork, line with baking paper and baking beans and bake for 15 minutes. Remove the paper and beans and bake for 5 minutes more or until golden. Turn down the oven to 180C/350F/gas 4.
2. Meanwhile, steam the sliced leeks for 5 minutes or until tender, then set aside. Mix the eggs with the milk and most of the Parmigiano Reggiano. Stir in the watercress and season well with black pepper.
3. Spread the steamed leeks over the base of the tart, then pour over the egg mixture, flake the salmon over the top and sprinkle with the remaining cheese. Bake on the preheated sheet for 25-30 minutes until the filling is just set and the pastry is golden. Serve warm or chilled, in wedges with green salad.
Recipe and photograph from Waitrose. More than 5,000 recipes can be found at www.waitrose.com/recipes

THIS WEEK'S TOP TIP
How to check your credit rating

MONEY
Three main agencies hold the majority of credit records: Experian, Equifax and Callcredit. When you apply for credit – anything from an actual credit card to a mobile phone contract to a mortgage – the company you are dealing with can check your rating via these agencies. At the same time, the company registers your new contract with the agency, and keeps them supplied with information (late payments, court orders etc). Your credit record is a simple statement of fact, but errors can occur, which is why it's advisable to check it. Ask each agency for a statutory report, for which it will charge a small fee. You need to contact them all, as information may be spread across all three.

ALL THINGS BRIGHT AND BEAUTIFUL
Wild roses
Sweet-scented dog roses are a familiar sight in our hedgerows. Left unchecked by hedge-cutting, a dog rose can scramble through adjoining trees to flower exotically at the top. They often turn up in old gardens, where they've been used as grafting stock for more delicate varieties that have then died, allowing the vigorous dog-rose rootstock to take over.

DON'T QUOTE ME, BUT...
'A diplomat is a man who always remembers a woman's birthday, but never remembers her age'
Robert Frost

SHIP WRECKED
St Mary's lighthouse didn't always do its job

ST MARY'S ISLAND
nr Whitley Bay, Tyne and Wear
Size: 0.75 acres
Population: 1 family

Expeditions to see St Mary's Island have been enjoyed by day-trippers ever since the railway came to Whitley Bay in 1882. Today there's a jolly collection of buildings – the bright white lighthouse, a red-roofed cottage, a larger handsome house behind.

A wide concrete causeway leads over to them and the sandstone rock, 300 million years old, on which they stand. Touring cyclists weave cautiously around ice cream-licking holidaymakers while, during term time, primary-school children out on a trip gabble their way across. This is definitely not one of those islands to which only the adventurous and the bold obtain access.

In the Middle Ages, you were most likely to spend time here if you were dead. Monks from Tynemouth Priory used the islet as a burial ground and founded a chapel dedicated not to St Mary, as might be imagined, but in fact to St Helen. This place of worship also served as an unofficial lighthouse since sailors were alerted to the presence of the rock by a light that was kept burning in a window.

In 1799 Russian soldiers en route to the Napoleonic Wars were stricken with cholera and swiftly quarantined on the island. Only the very fortunate survived. Those who didn't were buried alongside the long-dead monks. The cemetery itself is now buried and human bones are sometimes unearthed in the course of building works.

The chapel has gone, too, though it continues to live on in essence since its stones were used in a small croft constructed in 1855 by a fisherman called George Ewen. When laws governing salmon fishing changed, Ewen had to diversify and he turned the croft into an inn called The Freemason's Arms, which proved an instant hit due to the fact that, when the tide was in, the local constabulary was kept at bay. It's a private residence again nowadays and the two former lighthouse keepers' cottages now house the visitor centre and shop, so, when the causeway is covered, the island's sole inhabitants have the place to themselves.

The lighthouse built in 1896 couldn't save every passing ship, as is only too evident at low tide when part of the keel of the California, a Russian four-masted iron barque, can be seen. The ship was driven onto the rocks in a storm in January 1913 with the loss of eight lives. It's safe to say that St Mary's hasn't been a happy place for Russians.

HOW TO GET THERE
Hop off the train at Newcastle, then take the Metro to Whitley Bay, from where the no 308 or 309 bus will take you as far as Whitley Bay Cemetery. Then it's just a half-mile walk to the causeway. The island is open for only a few hours a day (and not every day) between May and September. It is also usually open most Saturdays and Sundays from October to April, as well as on certain other dates. Before setting out, it's best to check.

THIS WEEK'S TOP TIP
Don't be brow beaten

BEAUTY

There's nothing so ageing as over-plucked eyebrows that have then been redrawn. It really is worth getting a professional shape and groom that you can then follow up at home. Once you've got your brows into shape, boost any sparse areas with light upward pencil strokes in a shade that matches your hair. To add more colour and definition, use a brush and powder shadow.

RECIPE OF THE WEEK
Sticky Lemon Chicken with Cucumber & Coriander Salsa
Serves 4

Prepare 10 mins **Cook** 30 mins
4 essential Waitrose British Chicken Thighs
Juice and grated zest of 1 lemon, plus wedges to serve
2 tbsp clear honey
2 cloves garlic, crushed
1 cucumber portion, halved, seeded and sliced
1 small red onion, thinly sliced
4 Waitrose Cornichons, thinly sliced
½ x 28g pack coriander, roughly chopped

1. Preheat the oven to 200C/400F/gas 6. Place the chicken in a small baking dish. Mix together the lemon zest and juice, honey and garlic, then pour over the chicken. Bake for 30 minutes until golden and sticky and cooked through with no pink meat, covering with foil if the chicken starts to get too brown.
2. To make the salsa, mix together the cucumber, red onion, cornichons and coriander. Serve the chicken with the salsa and lemon wedges, spooning over any juices.
Recipe and photograph from Waitrose. More than 5,000 recipes can be found at www.waitrose.com/recipes

DON'T QUOTE ME, BUT...
'One of the many things nobody ever tells you about middle age is that it's such a nice change from being young'
William Feather

ALL THINGS BRIGHT AND BEAUTIFUL
Beautiful demoiselle
The wings of the male beautiful demoiselle (a type of damselfly) are an extraordinary deep navy blue. You're most likely to spot them close to water, especially streams with sandy bottoms – their larvae are aquatic. Like dragonflies, the males are territorial, chasing away rivals. Unlike dragonflies, demoiselles and damselflies always rest with their wings along the body – they're also smaller.

UNEXPECTED ANNIVERSARIES
TIME FOR TEA?
June 2014 is the 173rd anniversary of... the opening of the London-Bristol route on the Great Western Railway

The 99-year lease of the refreshment rooms at Swindon station *(top)* contained a clause obliging the GWR to stop all trains there for ten minutes so that the passengers could buy refreshments. At first this didn't make much difference to anybody, but as the service developed, the delay became more and more inconvenient until, in 1895, the lease was bought back for £100,000 – a full refund. Until then, though, everybody had to have tea in Swindon.

Isambard Kingdom Brunel *(above)* immediately kicked off the great tradition of moaning about railway catering, writing this letter to complain about the coffee at Swindon. *Dear Sir, I assure you [the manager] was wrong in supposing that I thought you purchased inferior coffee. I thought I said to him that I was surprised you should buy such bad roasted corn. I did not believe that you had such a thing as coffee in the place; I am certain that I never tasted any. I have long ceased to make complaints at Swindon. I avoid taking anything there when I can help it. Yours faithfully, I K Brunel*

'The arts cuts are starting to bite.'

WOTEVA!
Teenage translator

Bounce
To get going, on the move

Itchin'
To want something so badly that you are, erm, itching for it. Go on, have a good scratch, you know you deserve it

Rents
How teens refer to their parents. The fact that the word also suggests a never-ending dripping away of cash for no return of substance is purely coincidental

PET OF THE MONTH
Feed me

Name: Polycat
Owner's name: Ben Pierce
Best habit: Doesn't chase birds
(can't be bothered)
Worst habit: Conning anyone
who walks into the kitchen that she
hasn't been fed for hours
Likes: Sitting on the shed roof
in the sunshine
Dislikes: Smoked salmon
Personality: Reincarnation
of Queen Nefertiti
Naughtiest moment: Hides the
evidence too well
Most human trait: Being a bit
of a girly cat, faces away from the
TV when football's on

TOP TECHIE TIP
Scam stoppers

It's crucial to keep a watchful eye for
scammers when you're online. A few
basic checks and a bit of research of
your own is a good idea. Check the
'who is' of websites: www.whois.net
will tell you the registrants of all the
top-level domain names, such as .com
and .org. The site www.nic.uk will do
the same for sites ending in co.uk.
Googling a phrase from a website is
an excellent way to find out if the
content has been lifted from a
genuine or a cloned website.
Scammers will set up fake sites to fool
you, but they will rarely create a
complicated multi-page site or
originate all the content themselves.

HOW TO MAKE
DECORATED COAT HANGERS

**Decorated coat hangers make a lovely present, particularly if personalised
with the recipient's name – or if they specify which garment they are for**

WHAT YOU'LL NEED
Wooden coat hangers, gloss paint, paint brushes

WHAT TO DO
1. To ensure a good finish, use
a couple of coats of gloss paint in
your chosen colour, and allow to dry
completely before adding a design or
name in a contrasting colour.
2. Use as little paint as is needed to
create an even coverage and flat
finish – this will also keep drips to
a minimum. When applying the
background colour, paint the entire
coat hanger and then hang it on
a clothesline (or similar) to dry, with
a few sheets of newspaper placed
underneath to catch any drips.

JOKE OF THE MONTH
A man takes his cross-eyed dog to the vet. 'Is there anything you can do for him?' he asks.
'Let's take a look at him,' says the vet. He picks the
dog up, examines his eyes, then checks his teeth.
Finally, he says: 'I'm going to have to put him down.'
'What? Because he's cross-eyed?'
'No, because he's really heavy.'
sent in by John Peterson

USE IT OR LOSE IT
BRAIN EXERCISE
Give your grey matter a work-out

SUDOKU
The game of logic. Place each of the digits 1 to 9 in each row, column and 3x3 box. There is only one solution.

						7		
	3	8					4	
9	4			2	1			
9			6	7		5		
6			4		2			8
	7			8	5			6
		1	3			4	2	
1				9	3			
	2							

GRAMMAR CHALLENGE
The Lynne Truss test Can you spot the errors in grammar, punctuation and spelling? See below for the correct version.

can you distinguish between butterflies and moths you can try these two rules but while they generally work they are not foolproof as both belong to the order lepidoptera first there are the antennae butterflies tend to have matchstick shaped antennae straight with a blob on the top whereas moths usually have long tapering antennae sometimes highly feathered especially for males for use in finding mates second there is the question of resting wings butterflies tend to fold there wings upright on their backs like a book moths fold their wings flat like a jet fighter

JUNE'S GENERAL KNOWLEDGE QUIZ
1. Which of these England squad players did not play in a single game during the 1966 World Cup?
A. Terry Paine, B. Ian Callaghan,
C. George Eastham, D. John Connelly

2. Which of these was not a designated British beach-head on D-Day in 1944?
A. Juno, B. Sword, C. Nelson, D. Gold

3. *June is Bustin' Out All Over* comes from which musical?
A. *Oklahoma*, B. *Carousel*, C. *Seven Brides for Seven Brothers*, D. *South Pacific*

4. The Seventies sitcom *Terry and June* was set in which South London suburb?
A. Purley, B. Wimbledon, C. Cheam, D. Bromley

5. Juneau is the state capital of...
A. Nebraska, B. Wyoming, C. Alaska, D. Maine

6. Bloomsday on June 16 celebrates what?
A. The works of James Joyce, B. The Dublin Flower Show,
C. Jewish food in London, D. The writing of Ursula Bloom

7. At which London stadium did Henry Cooper first fight Cassius Clay in 1963?
A. White Hart Lane, B. Highbury, C. Wembley,
D. Loftus Road

8. Which comedy actor officially opened Britain's first ATM in June 1967?
A. Sid James, B. Reg Varney, C. Kenneth Williams,
D. Tony Hancock

9. Who led the Peasants' Revolt in 1381?
A. Wat Tyler, B. Jack Cade, C. Thomas Wintour,
D. Francis Tresham

10. Who attacked the English fleet based at Chatham, Kent, in June 1667?
A. The French, B. The Spanish, C. The Dutch,
D. The Portuguese

Can you distinguish between butterflies and moths? You can try these two rules, but while they generally work, they are not foolproof as both belong to the order Lepidoptera. First, there are the antennae: butterflies tend to have matchstick-shaped antennae (straight with a blob on the top); whereas moths usually have long, tapering antennae, sometimes highly feathered (especially for males for use in finding mates). Second, there is the question of resting wings: butterflies tend to fold their wings upright on their backs, like a book; moths fold their wings flat, like a jet fighter.

ANSWERS
1. C, 2. C,
3. B, 4. A,
5. C, 6. A,
7. C, 8. B,
9. A, 10. C

6	8	2	1	3	4	7	5	9
2	4	1	7	8	6	3	9	5
3	6	8	1	2	5	4	7	9
4	1	5	3	7	9	8	2	6
8	7	9	2	1	4	5	6	3
9	3	6	5	8	7	2	5	4
5	2	4	6	3	1	9	7	8
7	4	3	8	5	2	6	1	4
3	5	7	4	8	6	9	1	7

JULY 2014

A VIEW FROM THE 18th CENTURY
The bridge at Stourhead, Wiltshire
Photograph by Saga Magazine
reader Wendy Smith

JULY

1
Tuesday
🔵 **Opening** **The First World War Galleries**
Imperial War Museum, London

2
Wednesday

3
Thursday
🔵 **Retrospective** **Kazimir Malevich,** painter
Tate Modern, Bankside, London (to Oct 19)

4
Friday

5
Saturday

6
Sunday

7
Monday

8
Tuesday
🔵 **Gardening** **RHS Hampton Court Palace Flower Show**
Hampton Court, Surrey (to July 13)

9
Wednesday

10
Thursday

11
Friday

12
Saturday

13
Sunday

14
Monday **Bank Holiday, NI**

15
Tuesday

16
Wednesday

17
Thursday

18
Friday

Saga Magazine has everything you need to fill your days

Diary looking a bit empty this month? Pick up your copy of Saga and turn to the Out There pages.
Every month we give you details of events all over the country, from music festivals to literary
get-togethers, celebratory anniversaries and days out. We review the latest films and give you the lowdown
on what everyone's talking about – from plays, musicals and dance, to unmissable exhibitions.
And you can find even more online at **www.saga.co.uk/magazine**. To subscribe call 0800 056 1057
or go to **www.saga.co.uk/magazine-subscriptions**

19
Saturday

20
Sunday

21
Monday

22
Tuesday

23
Wednesday

24
Thursday

25
Friday

26
Saturday

27
Sunday

28
Monday

29
Tuesday

30
Wednesday

31
Thursday

DECADE BUSTERS

JULY
BIRTHDAYS

TURNING 70
Jonathan Dimbleby
broadcaster

TURNING 60
Neil Tennant *singer/songwriter*
(The Pet Shop Boys)

TURNING 50
Sandra Bullock
(right) American
actress
Bonnie Langford
entertainer

RECIPE OF THE WEEK
Baked Eggs with Creamy Nutmeg Spinach
Serves 2

Prepare 10 mins **Cook** 15 mins
250g pack essential Waitrose Spinach
25g (1oz) butter
1 tbsp plain flour
150ml (¼ pint) semi-skimmed milk
¼ tsp grated nutmeg
4 Waitrose Columbian Blacktail medium free-range eggs
2 tbsp Waitrose Half Fat Crème Fraîche
Grated vegetarian Cheddar, to serve (optional)

1. Preheat the oven to 200C/400F/gas 6. Cook the spinach in boiling water for 1 minute, drain and refresh under cold water. Squeeze out all the water with your hands and chop finely. Heat the butter in a small pan, add the flour and cook for 1 minute. Off the heat, stir in the milk a little at a time, then bring to the boil and stir until thick and smooth.
2. Stir the chopped spinach into the sauce and add nutmeg and seasoning. Spoon into 2 large ramekins (250ml/9fl oz or larger) or shallow gratin dishes. Make shallow wells in the spinach, then break 2 eggs into each. Spoon over the crème fraîche and scatter with the grated Cheddar, if using.
3. Place in a roasting tin filled with hot water and bake in the oven for 12-15 minutes until the eggs are set. Serve with crusty bread.
Recipe and photograph from Waitrose. More than 5,000 recipes can be found at www.waitrose.com/recipes

THIS WEEK'S TOP TIP
Deadheading

GARDENING
To ensure flowering plants carry on blooming, the trick is to keep on deadheading. Snip off flowers the minute they've passed their best and before they've had a chance to start forming seed pods. All plants are programmed to produce seed and if you keep interrupting that process, they'll carry on producing more flowers in the attempt to do so.

If you've nerves of steel, you can stage-manage how your garden performs even further by cutting down some plants just as they are about to flower. This technique produces sturdier plants that are less prone to flopping over and will flower later in the year.

ALL THINGS BRIGHT AND BEAUTIFUL
Wild cherries
Cherries are edge-of-woodland trees as they need the light to grow properly. Towards the end of July the fruit should be fully ripe and in a bumper year, if you can beat the birds, mice and squirrels, you can pick enough for a pie or for your own home-made cherry brandy (follow the principle for sloe gin in November). Even a handful on a country walk makes a refreshing snack.

DON'T QUOTE ME, BUT...
'After 30, a body has a mind of its own'
Bette Midler

A very 19th-century obsession

Whatever you may feel about stuffed animals and birds, there's no doubt that fine specimens fetch good money at auction. We get the lowdown

Although many disapprove of the Victorian passion for shooting and stuffing wildlife, there's been a revival of interest in taxidermy. Perhaps Damien Hirst is to blame. His shark in formaldehyde was a notable success and other contemporary artists such as Polly Morgan have their own modern take on this 19th-century obsession.

Most medium-sized towns would have had taxidermy shops 150 years ago and many examples of their wares still exist. Animals were recreated using wool and wire and their skins were often coated with arsenic to keep insects at bay. Among notable firms are James Gardner, who supplied Queen Victoria, and John Cooper and Sons, who specialised in fish. Examples from both fetch several hundred pounds at auction today.

After the First World War, when taxidermy fell out of fashion, many stuffed animals were thrown away. Despite the arsenic, others will have succumbed to moth damage and insect attack. But good examples,

especially of rare or extinct specimens, are highly sought after by collectors, whatever reservations others might have about these curious reminders of our imperial past.

SOLD

This octagonal case containing 30 exotic birds dates from about 1880 and sold for £1,729 at Sworders in Essex, July 2010

REDISCOVERED BOOK

'A whole spectrum of colours and lights'

A House in Flanders
Michael Jenkins
(Slightly Foxed Paperback, £11)

In 1951, the shy and solitary 14-year-old Michael Jenkins was sent by his parents to spend the summer with 'the aunts in Flanders'. So began the formative experience that, when he finally came to write about it half a century later, reappeared to him 'as in a dream, complete but surreal'. In the words of Dirk Bogarde, 'A House in Flanders is a radiant book. A whole spectrum of colours and lights, of delights and elegances, of wistfulness and love.'

As chosen by the staff of Slightly Foxed bookshop, specialists in unusual titles, old and new; www.foxedbooks.com

'I think we need to check the rules.'

RECIPE OF THE WEEK
Spaghetti Carbonara with Courgette & Fresh Basil
Serves 2

Prepare 10 mins **Cook** 20 mins
150g essential Waitrose Spaghetti
Knob of butter
1 clove garlic, crushed
1 shallot, finely chopped
1 large courgette, coarsely grated
½ x 25g pack fresh basil
2 free-range eggs
100g (4oz) Waitrose Crème Fraîche
25g (1oz) grated Parmigiano Reggiano, plus extra to serve

1. Cook the pasta in a large pan of boiling water according to pack instructions.
2. Meanwhile, heat the butter in a frying pan and cook the garlic, shallot and courgette for 6–8 minutes until softened and slightly golden. Set aside a few small basil leaves and shred the remainder. Stir the shredded basil into the courgette mixture and cook for a few seconds.
3. Beat together the eggs, crème fraîche, Parmigiano Reggiano and some coarse black pepper.
4. Drain the pasta and return to the pan (off the heat). Add the courgette and egg mixtures to the pan and toss well together until the heat of the pasta has thickened the sauce. Divide between two bowls, scatter with the basil leaves and a little more Parmigiano Reggiano to serve.
Recipe and photograph from Waitrose. More than 5,000 recipes can be found at www.waitrose.com/recipes

THIS WEEK'S TOP TIP
Take another bite of the cherry

HEALTH
Gout sufferers may reduce attacks by eating cherries or drinking cherry juice. US researchers found that patients with gout who ate 10-12 cherries over a two-day period had a 35% lower risk of attacks compared with those who did not. It's thought the fruit contains anthocyanins, which contain anti-inflammatory properties.
   Luckily, frozen or canned cherries are just as good if you can't find the fresh variety, and the darker they are, the better.

ALL THINGS BRIGHT AND BEAUTIFUL
Grasshoppers
At the height of summer you can hardly walk through long grass without sending up a cloud of grasshoppers. And the 'chirping' noise they make is synonymous with hot weather. They create the sound by rubbing their hind legs against their forewings – a process known as stridulation. The meadow grasshopper *(above)* is the commonest of our native 30 species but, unlike the others, it is flightless.

DON'T QUOTE ME, BUT...
'He taught me housekeeping; when I divorce, I keep the house'
Zsa Zsa Gabor

BADGER'S BLOG
'I'M NOT VERY GOOD AT DOING WHAT I'M TOLD'

That's particularly the case for Badger when unfavourable comparisons are being made – and she is found wanting

BOG was reading aloud from the paper. Apparently someone called the 'pope' is very keen on a foreign dog called a 'Dogo Argentino'. 'It's a famous Argentinian breed prized for its loyalty and placid temperament,' he read to GOB (who wasn't looking exactly gripped). 'They call it the Great White Dog,' he continued. 'It has the following qualities: protective, loyal, good natured, friendly, obedient, affectionate, tolerant.' Then he looked at me in a way that I can describe only as 'disappointed'.

When I was small the DFLs brought in the first of many dog trainers and just before he left, saying that I was 'virtually untrainable', he told them I was 'two predators for the price of one: half scent dog and half sight dog'. As they waved him off, BOG patted me on the head and said he'd never been prouder of me.

Next I was banned from puppy class for 'disruptive' behaviour, herding the other dogs under a table and knocking out one of Elvis the Alsatian's teeth. As we were shown the door, he wiped his eye and told me he was proud of me again.

So I must be doing something good – even though I don't particularly want to be good. The problem is that I'm not very good at doing what I'm told. On one occasion, for example, he was proudly telling some visitors that what distinguished dogs from all other animals (apart from humans) was that they understood 'hand gestures'. 'Allow me to demonstrate with Badger,' he said pompously, leading us all into the garden. 'You will choose an object, any object, and I will point at it. Badger will follow where I am pointing and go and investigate.' The visitors chose a plastic leprechaun, BOG pointed at it, and I ran in the opposite direction.

He shouldn't have compared me insultingly to a Dogo.

Name this month: *Dogo Wogo*
Best moment: *showing him up in front of the visitors. HAR HAR RUFF!*

JULY
DRINK OF THE MONTH

PIÑA COLADA

Serve this and bring back happy memories of exotic holidays

1 cup crushed ice
45ml (1½fl oz) white rum
15ml (½fl oz) coconut cream
15ml (½fl oz) Malibu
100ml (3½fl oz) pineapple juice
15ml (½fl oz) sugar syrup
Pineapple leaves

Place the crushed ice, rum, coconut cream, Malibu, pineapple juice and sugar syrup in a blender and whiz until the mixture is the consistency of shaved ice. Pour into a large, chilled cocktail glass and garnish with pineapple leaves and a cocktail umbrella.

Sit!
This is me when I was small and better behaved

RECIPE OF THE WEEK
Tennessee Steak & Blue Cheese Salad
Serves 2

Prepare 20 mins **Cook** 10 mins
300g (11oz) essential Waitrose British Beef Sirloin Steak or Hereford Beef Sirloin Steak
1 clove garlic, crushed
2 tbsp Jack Daniel's Tennessee Whiskey
50g (2oz) Waitrose Cave Aged Roquefort AOP
3 tbsp essential Waitrose Half Fat Soured Cream
100g (4oz) Waitrose Trimmed Fine Green Beans
4 thick slices Waitrose Mixed Olive Ciabatta
1 tbsp olive oil
1 sweet Dolce Verde Romaine Lettuce, roughly torn
2 tbsp snipped chives

1. Place the steak in a shallow dish and rub in the crushed garlic. Pour the Jack Daniel's whiskey over the meat and leave to marinate for 15 minutes.
2. Meanwhile, roughly mash the Roquefort, then stir in the soured cream. Place in the fridge until ready to serve.
3. Cook the green beans in a pan of boiling water, then drain and cool.
4. Lightly brush the bread with oil. Lift the steak out of the marinade, shaking off any excess. Cook the bread and steak over hot coals or in a griddle pan for 2-3 minutes on each side (the bread may be a bit quicker), until both are nicely browned and the steak is still a little pink in the centre.
5. Place the lettuce and green beans in a large serving bowl. Tear the toasted bread into pieces and add to the bowl. Slice or cube the steak and add to the salad. Spoon the blue cheese dressing on top, sprinkle with chives and serve.
Recipe and photograph from Waitrose. More than 5,000 recipes can be found at www.waitrose.com/recipes

THIS WEEK'S TOP TIP
Check your tax code

MONEY
It's up to you to check that you're paying the correct amount of tax – it's not HMRC's responsibility. And the penalties can be tough if it turns out that you've been underpaying. If you're over 60 and on a low income, you should be able to get advice from the charity Tax Help for Older People: visit their website at www.taxvol.org.uk or call 01308 488066.

DON'T QUOTE ME, BUT...
'My notion of a wife at 40 is that a man should be able to change her, like a bank note, for two 20s'
Warren Beatty

ALL THINGS BRIGHT AND BEAUTIFUL
Dragonflies
One of our commonest dragonflies is the broad-bodied chaser. The males are territorial, patrolling 'their' area of a pond and launching an attack against any incoming males. As the name suggests, this species is quite stocky. Males have a powder-blue abdomen, females a yellowy-brown one. Dragonfly larvae are aquatic, spending two to three years underwater before metamorphosing: climbing out onto a nearby plant stem and performing incredible contortions, the adult emerging from the spent shell of the larva. There were dragonflies doing the same thing 350 million years ago.

CONSPIRACY PLOT
The Scottish island that has seen its share of clan warfare

CARA
Off Gigha, Argyll
Size: 163 acres
Population: 0

Cara is an island under the unofficial lairdship of a Brownie. This is not a small girl working towards her home skills badge but 'a neat little man, dressed in brown, with a pointed beard', according to a description given in 1909 by Morton Macdonald of Largie, who also pointed out that the man was 'not recorded in any census'.

As you might have guessed, he's the spirit of a Macdonald of ages past who was murdered by a Campbell, the clan that gives treachery a bad name. Just off the west coast of the Kintyre peninsula, Cara (Gaelic for 'dear one' or 'dear friend') is the dot to the long exclamation mark that is Gigha ('God's Island'). At first sight, it doesn't look much – a treeless island that rises abruptly in the south. There's one house that no one could describe as beautiful. Built around 1733, it serves today as the holiday home for its leaseholder.

However, scratch beneath the surface, and it's more intriguing than its appearance suggests. For a start, it has attracted settlers for aeons. The brace of interconnecting caves in the cliffs at the southern end of the isle show signs of human habitation of indistinct origin, but one can assume they're fairly venerable. We also know that Viking boots have almost certainly trodden its soil.

Cara became entangled in a dispute between the Macdonalds and (inevitably) the Campbells in 1615. Kinsmen who threw in their lots with Sir James Macdonald made Cara their base as they plotted to capture Hector MacNeill of Taynish and Gigha, allied to the Argyll Campbells. MacNeill duly sent a party to raid the island but the Macdonalds, warned by beacon from the mainland, saw them off, though they were routed themselves some time later. Tradition has it that MacNeill and some Campbell lords had dinner in the mansion house and for dessert hanged eight Macdonalds. If so, they were not the only men to come to an untimely end on Cara – the brother of Flora MacDonald (she of Bonnie Prince Charlie fame) was killed in a shooting accident on the island.

Cara is still owned by the Macdonalds of Largie. With rocks strewn about it, it has claimed more than its fair share of shipwrecks. It cannot, however, be blamed for the loss of the Aska on September 22, 1940. The new ship, loaded with copra (coconut kernels), received a direct hit from a bomb dropped by a German plane. She drifted into the bay on the west side of the island and burned brightly for six weeks.

The island's precariously small population had given up the unequal struggle ten years beforehand, leaving Cara to the rabbits and feral goats that still graze the island today.

HOW TO GET THERE
Probably the least stressful way is to take the train to Glasgow, then board the no 926 bus with a sturdy book. Around three-and-a-half hours later, alight at Tayinloan. Here a ferry (hourly from 8am to 7pm in summer) will take you over to the isle of Gigha, landing in Ardminish Bay. Enquire at the nearby post office if there's anyone with a boat in the water who will ferry you over to Cara.

RECIPE OF THE WEEK
Layered Summer Pudding with Blackberries & Strawberries
Serves 6

Prepare 15 mins + chilling time **Cook** 5 mins
4 x 150g packs essential Waitrose Dessert Blackberries
225g (8oz) strawberries, sliced
3 tbsp crème de cassis
25g (1oz) caster sugar
1 tbsp chopped fresh mint
7 slices (about 170g/6oz) medium, preferably stale,
*   white bread, crusts removed*
Clotted cream (optional), to serve

1. Place the fruit, crème de cassis and sugar into a large saucepan and cook on a medium heat for 5 minutes. Set aside to cool. Stir through the mint, then drain in a sieve, reserving the juice.
2. Soak the bread in the reserved juice and place a third in the base of an 18cm (7in) square dish. Top with half the fruit and mint mixture and spread evenly to the edge of the bread, then repeat the layers, finishing with a layer of bread.
3. Cover with clingfilm, press down and place a plate with a weight on top. Chill for 3-4 hours, or ideally overnight.
4. Cut into 6 slices and serve with clotted cream, if using, and any leftover juice.
Recipe and photograph from Waitrose. More than 5,000 recipes can be found at www.waitrose.com/recipes

THIS WEEK'S TOP TIP
Ooh la la French manicure

BEAUTY
One of the easiest beauty boosts to try at home is a French manicure. All you need is a nail buffer to smooth out ridges and apply a shine – there's no need to apply clear varnish unless you really want to. Then finish off with a white nail pencil, applying it under the tips of the nails for that chic French effect.

DON'T QUOTE ME, BUT...
'A stockbroker urged me to buy a stock that would triple its value every year. I told him, "At my age, I don't even buy green bananas"'
Claude Pepper

ALL THINGS BRIGHT AND BEAUTIFUL
Pheasant chicks
Neatly camouflaged pheasant chicks know that their best chances of survival are to stand stock still and rely on becoming indistinguishable from their background. Unlike garden-bird species, whose chicks hatch blind and naked from the egg, pheasant chicks hit the ground running: their eyes are open and they are able to feed immediately. The scientific term for this is nidifugous – literally 'flee the nest'.

UNEXPECTED ANNIVERSARIES
RED OR GREEN?
July 2014 is the 170th anniversary of:
the death of John Dalton

Chemist and physicist John Dalton (*above*) discovered colour-blindness in the following way: he bought his mother, a Quaker, a pair of stockings for her birthday. She was shocked because they were bright red and so quite inappropriate. He refused to believe her – they looked dark brown to him – until the neighbours confirmed it. The genetic nature of the condition was suggested to him by the fact that his brother also described the stockings as brown. Red/green colour-blindness is still referred to as daltonism today.

Dalton's theory about his colour-blindness was that the liquid in his eyes was tinted blue. To test this idea, he left instructions that his assistant Joseph Ransome should dissect his eyes after his death. As instructed, Ransome in due course cut a hole in one eyeball and squeezed out the liquid – demonstrating that the theory was wrong.

'Ah, de Groot! Master of the unguarded moment!'

WOTEVA!
Teenage translator

Ding
Phone me. A quaint hark back to ancient history and the ringing telephone. How do they know?

Fake bake
An artificial tan

Proper bo
When something is really good, and works perfectly

PET OF THE MONTH
Savage hamster

Name: Stripe
Owner's name: Elizabeth Schwartz
Best habit: Running on wheel
so fast he revolves with it
Worst habit: Savaging his owner's
hand the minute it enters his cage
Likes: Peanut butter
Dislikes: Humans, other hamsters
Personality: Belligerent to homicidal
Naughtiest moment:
Attacking his brother, causing a vet's
bill longer than the hamster itself
Most human trait:
Enjoys having an ASBO

TOP TECHIE TIP
Quick response

Over the past couple of years, we bet you've noticed the proliferation of those black and white chequered squares appearing on posters, advertisements and even on some supermarket products. These barcode-like designs are called QR or Quick Response codes. They work with your mobile phone's camera to take you immediately to a website providing information about the event, product or service being advertised. Sometimes the QR code will lead you to a money-off voucher you can use at a checkout, without the bother of printing it out beforehand. To access QR codes you'll need to download a special app to your phone – there are dozens of these available free on the iPhone and Android phone app markets (QR Reader and ScanLife are two of the most popular ones).

HOW TO MAKE
A VINTAGE BIRTHDAY BANNER

There is something very appealing about old fonts and typefaces, and vintage letter cards lend a unique feel to birthday banners. String them together to say 'Happy Birthday!' or 'Welcome home' loud and clear to a loved one

WHAT YOU'LL NEED
Letter playing cards
String or ribbon
Hole punch
Scissors

WHAT TO DO
1. Punch 2 holes at the top of each letter card approximately 1cm (½in) from each side.
2. Thread the string or ribbon through each card from back to front, then hang your party decoration.

Alternatively, pack the threaded pieces together and post the banner to an appreciative friend!

TIPS
The possibilities are limitless – you can use these cards to spell out anything from 'Happy Christmas/Easter/Anniversary' to 'I love you', 'Be my Valentine', 'Thank you' or simply someone's name. Vintage letter cards are usually available from online auction sites; if you don't want to buy a set, just trace letters from any vintage publication onto plain cards. This will allow you to choose the background colour too. If you do buy a whole pack, remember that individual cards can be used as single-initial birthday cards – so those not used in your banner won't be wasted.

JOKE OF THE MONTH
My wife was hinting about what she wanted for our impending anniversary. She said: 'I want something shiny that goes from 0 to 150 in about 3 seconds.' **So I bought her some scales.**

sent in by John Sanderson

USE IT OR LOSE IT
BRAIN EXERCISE
Give your grey matter a work-out

SUDOKU
The game of logic. Place each of the digits 1 to 9 in each row, column and 3x3 box. There is only one solution.

1	6			8				
		3				9	6	
	5		3	9			8	
5					3	6		
2								8
		4	9					7
	7			1	8		2	
	4	8				7		
			5				4	6

GRAMMAR CHALLENGE
The Lynne Truss test Can you spot the errors in grammar, punctuation and spelling? See below for the correct version.

for me july means golf for the past umpteen years i have written about the annual open championship for a national newspaper something i undertake in full awareness of my lack of credentials for the job every july i head of to st andrews carnoustie or sandwich every july when we meet in the press tent i say to the papers golf correspondant well here we are again hooray you couldnt just remind me who won it last year could you and every july i cry thank god for waterproof trousers as the rain comes in horizontally from the sea

JULY'S GENERAL KNOWLEDGE QUIZ

1. Who was not a signatory to the American Declaration of Independence?
A. Thomas Jefferson, B. Benjamin Franklin, C. George Washington, D. John Hancock

2. Who did Virginia Wade beat to win the Women's Singles title at Wimbledon in 1977?
A. Chris Evert, B. Betty Stove, C. Evonne Goolagong, D. Rosie Casals

3. By what name do we also know *La Fête Nationale*?
A. De Gaulle's official birthday, B. French Honour Day, C. Liberation Day, D. Bastille Day

4. Elvis Costello sang which classic Beatles song at Live Aid in 1985?
A. *Help*, B. *All You Need Is Love*, C. *I Feel Fine*, D. *A Day in the Life*

5. Which radio show made its debut on July 12, 1939?
A. *ITMA*, B. *Educating Archie*, C. *Desert Island Discs*, D. *The Archers*

6. Tony Jacklin (b. July 1944) won which golf 'major' in 1970?
A. The Open, B. The Masters, C. The US Open, D. The PGA Championship

7. In which year was smoking banned in all indoor public places in the UK?
A. 2006, B. 2007, C. 2008, D. 2009

8. Actress Jean Marsh (b. June 1934) co-created which TV drama series?
A. *The House of Elliott*, B. *Juliet Bravo*, C. *The Duchess of Duke Street*, D. *The Onedin Line*

9. What attraction was officially opened in July, 1955?
A. Battersea Fun Fair, B. Disneyland, C. The Hollywood Walk of Fame, D. London Zoo penguin pool

10. In July 1930, the film *Dizzy Dishes* saw the debut of which cartoon character?
A. Olive Oyl, B. Betty Boop, C. Minnie Mouse, D. Little Orphan Annie

For me, July means golf. For the past umpteen years, I have written about the annual Open Championship for a national newspaper, something I undertake in full awareness of my lack of credentials for the job. Every July, I head off to St Andrews, Carnoustie or Sandwich; every July, when we meet in the press tent, I say to the paper's golf correspondent, 'Well, here we are again, hooray! You couldn't just remind me who won it last year, could you?' And every July I cry, 'Thank God for waterproof trousers!' as the rain comes in horizontally from the sea.

ANSWERS
1. C, 2. B,
3. D, 4. B,
5. A, 6. C,
7. B, 8. A,
9. B, 10. B

1	6	9	2	8	4	5	7	3
8	3	7	1	5	6	9	2	4
2	5	4	7	3	9	6	8	1
7	1	5	3	6	2	8	9	4
9	4	6	8	2	7	1	3	5
3	8	2	4	9	5	7	6	2
5	7	6	9	4	1	8	3	2
6	9	3	5	7	8	2	1	7
4	2	8	6	1	3	4	5	9

AWAITING THE TIDE
Wells-next-the-Sea, Norfolk
Photograph by Saga Magazine
reader Geoffrey Leng

AUGUST
2014

AUGUST

1
Friday

2
Saturday

3
Sunday

4
Monday
**Bank Holiday, Scotland. Centenary of the
first day of conflict in the First World War**

5
Tuesday

6
Wednesday

7
Thursday

8
Friday

9
Saturday

10
Sunday

11
Monday

12
Tuesday

13
Wednesday

14
Thursday

15
Friday

16
Saturday

17
Sunday

18
Monday

Saga Magazine has everything you need to fill your days

Diary looking a bit empty this month? Pick up your copy of Saga and turn to the Out There pages.
Every month we give you details of events all over the country, from music festivals to literary
get-togethers, celebratory anniversaries and days out. We review the latest films and give you the lowdown
on what everyone's talking about – from plays, musicals and dance, to unmissable exhibitions.
And you can find even more online at **www.saga.co.uk/magazine**. To subscribe call 0800 056 1057
or go to **www.saga.co.uk/magazine-subscriptions**

19
Tuesday

20
Wednesday

21
Thursday

22
Friday

23
Saturday

24
Sunday

25
Monday
Bank Holiday

26
Tuesday

27
Wednesday

28
Thursday

29
Friday

30
Saturday

31
Sunday

DECADE BUSTERS
AUGUST BIRTHDAYS

TURNING 70
John Simpson *TV news reporter*
Clive Lloyd *West Indian cricketer*

TURNING 60
Elvis Costello *(above) Irish singer*
Steve Wright *DJ*

TURNING 50
Melinda Gates
  American businesswoman and philanthropist
David Fincher *American director*

THIS WEEK'S TOP TIP
Look after your lavender

GARDENING

Lavender becomes woody and unattractive if not kept in trim by pruning. Prune it immediately it has finished flowering. If you leave the flowers on, the bush puts all its resources into making seed: if you then prune it hard, it quite often gives up and dies.

A good all-over trim in August gives plants time to put on some growth before winter. Trim it lightly again in spring for best results.

August is also a good time to take semi-ripe cuttings of this year's growth: the base of the cutting should be hard but the tip soft. Trim off lower leaves and tip and push the cuttings into a pot of compost. Use a plastic bag as a cloche.

RECIPE OF THE WEEK
Grilled Cod with Basil & Lemon Grass
Serves 2

Prepare 5 mins + 15 mins marinating **Cook** 8 mins
1 clove garlic, finely chopped
1 stick lemon grass, finely chopped
½ x 25g pack fresh basil, shredded
Large pinch of ground turmeric
4 tbsp Waitrose Organic Low Fat Natural Yogurt
2 Waitrose Line Caught Prime Icelandic Cod Fillets, skin-on, about 150g (5oz) each
150g pack Waitrose Mange Tout Peas

1. Mix together the garlic, lemon grass, basil, turmeric, yogurt and some seasoning. Spoon over to coat the cod and leave to marinate for 15 minutes. Arrange the cod fillets on a baking sheet.
2. Preheat the grill. Grill the fish for 3-4 minutes on each side, turning once until the flesh is firm and opaque. Lightly steam the mange tout. Place the cod on top of the mange tout and serve.
Recipe and photograph from Waitrose. More than 5,000 recipes can be found at www.waitrose.com/recipes

ALL THINGS BRIGHT AND BEAUTIFUL
Field vole

The field vole is probably our commonest mammal, yet is rarely seen because they are so hard to spot – they're small, grey brown and spend most of their time in long grass. And they need to stay well hidden because they are an important part of the diet of kestrels and owls, as well as foxes, weasels and stoats. Instead, you're more likely to see the pathways voles create between stems of grass.

DON'T QUOTE ME, BUT...
'Old age is 15 years older than I am'
Oliver Wendell Holmes

'Arriving in Paris, Mrs Harris is in for one or two surprises'

Mrs Harris Goes to Paris and **Mrs Harris Goes to New York**
Paul Gallico
(Bloomsbury, £7.99)

Ada Harris is a charlady par excellence. One day, when tidying Lady Dent's wardrobe, she decides she will treat herself to a designer dress. She scrimps and saves and finally has enough money for the trip to Paris to buy the dress of her dreams. Arriving at the House of Dior, Mrs Harris is in for one or two surprises, as are the residents of Paris. This volume also contains the equally entertaining story of Mrs Harris's trip to America.

As chosen by the staff of Slightly Foxed bookshop, specialists in unusual titles, old and new; www.foxedbooks.com

A return to Victorian values

As we make more effort at home to conserve water, you may have the eco-friendly alternative to the power shower lurking in your attic

Many Victorians would have a bath once a week, using a jug and bowl for their daily wash. These were normally placed alongside a soap dish on marble-topped washstands in the bedroom. A body wash with flannel would involve just a splash or two of hot water. Although many jug and bowl sets can be picked up for less than £50, some fine examples, which might have graced the guest rooms of country houses, can fetch much more.

Queen Elizabeth, the Queen Mother, was a great fan of Wemyss Ware from Scotland. Their sets, often decorated in a cabbage-rose pattern, can fetch several hundred pounds. More generally, sets could be multipurpose, with the bowls used to mix cakes and the jugs for wine-making.

In the periods of drought that seem to characterise most British summers, perhaps they could make a comeback.

The Victorians were certainly much less profligate with water than we are. So maybe you should consider dusting down your set rather than offering it for sale.

SOLD
This Wemyss tray fetched £1,950 at Lyon and Turnbull in Edinburgh in August 2012

RECIPE OF THE WEEK
Curried Sweet Potato with Sweetcorn & Avocado Salsa
Serves 4

Prepare 15 mins **Cook** 25-45 mins
650g (1lb 6oz) sweet potatoes
2 tbsp Waitrose Cooks' Ingredients Tikka Curry Paste
Juice of 1 lemon
1 tbsp sunflower oil
2 tbsp chopped fresh mint
4 tbsp natural yogurt
195g can essential Waitrose Sweetcorn, drained
1 ripe avocado, stoned, peeled and diced
6 salad onions, chopped

1. Light the barbecue or preheat the oven to 200C/400F/ gas 6. Scrub the sweet potatoes and cut them into 1cm (½in) slices. Mix the curry paste, half the lemon juice, sunflower oil and mint together in a large bowl. Stir in the yogurt and season.
2. Add the sweet potatoes to the curry paste mixture and mix well until coated. Arrange the sweet potato slices on the hot barbecue and cook for 20-25 minutes, turning regularly, until tender. Alternatively, arrange the slices in a single layer in a shallow roasting tin and cook in the oven for 45 minutes, turning once, until golden and cooked through.
3. Make the salsa by combining the remaining ingredients and serve with the potatoes.
Recipe and photograph from Waitrose. More than 5,000 recipes can be found at www.waitrose.com/recipes

THIS WEEK'S TOP TIP
Eat more tomatoes

HEALTH
Lycopene, the bright red pigment that gives tomatoes their colour, has various health benefits. Research has shown that lycopene is linked to a lower risk of prostate cancer and also that it may help to prevent the blood clots that can then go on to cause a stroke. A study carried out in Finland showed that men with the highest levels of lycopene were half as likely to have a stroke as men with the lowest levels. While processing foods tends to reduce their nutritional value, reducing vitamin C content, for example, canning tomatoes or turning them into ketchup or purée increases the availability of lycopene. So get in the kitchen and rustle up some spaghetti Bolognese.

ALL THINGS BRIGHT AND BEAUTIFUL
Glow-worm
This month is your last chance to spot a female glow-worm signalling to attract a mate with a pinpoint of bright green light – in fields, roadside verges, hedgerows and even gardens. It's such an extraordinary sight, as though someone has dropped an LED in the grass. In fact the female's brightly lit abdomen is due to bioluminescence, a chemical reaction. Once she's mated, she stops glowing.

DON'T QUOTE ME, BUT...
'All I ask is the chance to prove that money can't make me happy'
Spike Milligan

BADGER'S BLOG

'HE CAME STUMBLING DOWNSTAIRS IN HIS PYJAMAS'

The birds wake Badger, so it must be an emergency.
She demands to be let out, to deal with the situation

One morning the birds were making more noise than usual. I knew it could mean only one thing. FURBALL ALERT! So I did what any dog must do in those circumstances. I made a lot of noise myself. Obviously I don't have an alarm clock, but if the birds are awake, and I'm awake, that must mean the DFLs should be awake. BOG came stumbling down the stairs in his pyjama bottoms, rubbing his eyes, and grunting about it being 'not even six'. I could tell he wasn't happy with me, even though I was on full defensive alert mode.

So he let me out the back door and I charged round the side of the house and... there they were. GRRR. Bold as you like. Sitting on top of Myrtle our caravan, grooming themselves and inspecting their claws. Permit me to introduce Horace and Hyacinth, my new sworn enemies, brought in to replace the hapless Bob who'd gone missing a few months before.

Before you ask, no, this had nothing to do with me. He was so stupid he'd probably hitched a lift in the back of a delivery van and got lost somewhere 100 miles away. But that didn't stop me from getting the third degree from the DFLs. Believe me (and eventually they did) the evidence would have been all too plain to see if it had been me, although this didn't seem to be much of a comfort to Helen and Tony next door.

But anyway, back to the two Horrible H's. They're a couple of 're-homed' cats who are so stuck up you'd think they'd come from *Downton Abbey*, rather than from Mrs Gammond's bungalow round the corner.

Well, I wasn't having them in my garden, so I launched myself at the back of the caravan snarling in a frenzy. And – oh joy! – it worked. Horace tried to make a run for it, lost his grip on the roof and began to slide down the side. And guess who was waiting for him? But I hadn't counted on BOG appearing with a power hose, which he aimed at both of us as Horace hit the ground. Now, I love a hose as much as the next dog, but there's a time and a place. And this wasn't either. So both furballs got away. This time. I'm keeping a keen eye on the situation, as you might expect. GRRRR.

Name this month: *Pookles*
Best moment: *Caught a rat. It died. I kindly left it on the doorstep.*

RECIPE OF THE WEEK
Baked Peaches with an Orange & Almond Topping
Serves 4

Prepare 15 mins **Cook** 20-25 mins
4 ripe peaches, halved and stoned
Grated zest of ½ orange
50g (2oz) butter, softened
50g (2oz) caster sugar
1 Waitrose Columbian Blacktail medium free-range egg, beaten
50g (2oz) ground almonds
About 1 tbsp flaked almonds to scatter
2 tbsp amaretto liqueur or orange juice

1. Preheat the oven to 190C/375F/gas 5. Arrange the peach halves snugly in a baking dish, cut-side up.
2. Cream the orange zest with the butter and sugar until pale, then beat in the egg. Stir in the ground almonds. Spoon into the centre of the peaches, scatter with flaked almonds and pour over the amaretto, or orange juice.
3. Bake for 20-25 minutes until the peaches are soft and the topping is golden. Serve hot or cold with vanilla ice cream or crème fraîche.
Recipe and photograph from Waitrose. More than 5,000 recipes can be found at www.waitrose.com/recipes

THIS WEEK'S TOP TIP
Donate foreign currency

MONEY

Come back from holiday with a handful of Croatian kuna or Turkish lira? There's no need to leave small change languishing in a drawer: many charities will be happy to take it off your hands. Try dropping it off at your local high street charity shop or look out for collection points before you leave the airport on your way home.

Airlines such as British Airways and Virgin Atlantic also collect loose change on board. It's estimated that in any given year UK travellers have about £900 million in unused foreign currency lying around. Better to put it to good use!

ALL THINGS BRIGHT AND BEAUTIFUL
Toads

Although toads and frogs are superficially similar, you can identify toads by their warty skin and dull brown colour, and, if they're on land, you'll see that toads walk rather than leap. Toads are far more land-based than frogs; you'll tend to find them in damp garden corners, under logs or bricks – they return to the water mainly during the mating season early in the year. (Incidentally, toadspawn is laid in long strings, compared with large masses of frogspawn.) Toads eat worms, insect larvae and slugs.

DON'T QUOTE ME, BUT...

'Age does not protect you from love. But love, to some extent, protects you from age'

Anaïs Nin

TINY ISLANDS
GIVEN AN INCH

The Scottish island that the Mitford sisters inherited

and the four seasons compact themselves into an afternoon. It's also the best place for scanning the heavens for white-tailed sea eagles and the seas for frolicking dolphins. Walk towards the southern edge of the plateau and the flat roof of the four-storey house comes into view.

And so we come to the Mitfords, and in particular to Unity. Obsessed with her friend Adolf Hitler, Unity was in Munich on the day Britain declared war on Germany. She shot herself in the head but survived, arriving home in 1940 and moving up to Inch Kenneth to live with her mother, where she planned and re-planned her own funeral. It wasn't long in coming. She died of pneumococcal meningitis in 1948 at the age of 33.

When Lady Redesdale died, in 1963, the island came into the possession of her five surviving daughters. Jessica bought out the other sisters and hosted parties there. She sold it four years later to the current owners and the island breathed a little sigh and the birds sang on the Sabbath and the mice danced and peace returned.

INCH KENNETH
nr Balnahard, Isle of Mull
Inner Hebrides
Size: 136 acres
Population: 0

Inch Kenneth is an island in perpetual shade: not from any shadow cast over it by the huge Gribun Cliffs on nearby Mull, but by a single aristocratic family who owned it for less than three decades. Ever since Lord Redesdale bought the island on the eve of the Second World War, he and his wife, and more particularly their six daughters – the infamous Mitford sisters – have proved characters larger than Inch Kenneth itself, reducing it to 'that island the Mitfords owned'.

It's a pity, really, because prior to 1939 this little island had already lived a life worthy of any biographer's pen. Inch is a corruption of one of the many Gaelic words for island and the Kenneth in question is St Kenneth, who is reputed to have built a chapel there in AD565. St Kenneth seems to have had a fondness for petty-minded miracles, such as banishing mice who ate his shoes and causing birds to stop singing on the Sabbath.

The island was farmed by Iona's Augustinian community until around

1574. The history books remained blank for the next two centuries, until the coming of none other than Samuel Johnson and James Boswell. The pair visited in 1773 as guests of Sir Allan MacLean, Johnson noting that: 'Sir Allan related the American campaign, and in the evening one of the ladies played on her harpsichord, while Col and Mr Boswell danced a Scottish reel with the other.' Johnson reckoned that Sunday to be 'the most agreeable he had ever passed' – high praise indeed.

Casting out to the west we come to one of Inch Kenneth's four distinct worlds. The Humpies are stubby fingers of land that claw ineffectively at the sea. They serve as a complete contrast to the tranquil eastern extremity, where a sandy, shell-strewn beach spreads out towards low islets, home to grey seals and ringed plovers.

The high plateau, the third of Inch Kenneth's worlds, is the ideal place to discover just how prone the island is to the mutability of the local weather. Snow can tumble out of a sunny sky

HOW TO GET THERE

Take the train to Oban, then the ferry to Craignure on the Isle of Mull. Bus no 495 runs to Salen, where public transport more or less peters out. A taxi can usher you the rest of the way to Ulva Ferry (alternatively it's a 21-mile cycle ride from Craignure). From Ulva Ferry, Mull Charters runs occasional sailings to Inch Kenneth.

RECIPE OF THE WEEK
Mediterranean Roasted Halloumi with Basil Dressing
Serves 4

Prepare 10 mins **Cook** 30 mins
500g (1lb) essential Waitrose New Potatoes,
*   halved lengthways*
Pack of 3 essential Waitrose Mixed Peppers,
*   seeds removed, sliced*
1 tbsp lemon-infused olive oil
25g pack basil, stalks removed
Zest of ½ lemon, plus squeeze of juice
125g (4½oz) cherry tomatoes, halved
½ x 250g pack essential Waitrose Cypriot Light
*   Halloumi, thickly sliced*

1. Preheat the oven to 200C/400F/gas 6. Cook the potatoes in a pan of boiling water for 5 minutes or until just tender. Drain, then tip into a large, shallow roasting tin and scatter over the sliced peppers.
2. Place the olive oil, basil leaves, lemon zest and juice in a small blender with some seasoning and blend until coarsely chopped. Pour the mixture over the vegetables and toss to coat. Roast for 20 minutes.
3. Turn up the heat to 220C/425F/gas 7. Add the halved tomatoes and sliced halloumi to the tray and roast for a further 5-10 minutes or until the cheese is golden brown. Serve straightaway.
Recipe and photograph from Waitrose. More than 5,000 recipes can be found at www.waitrose.com/recipes

THIS WEEK'S TOP TIP
The best make-up for a hot summer day

BEAUTY
If you want your make-up to survive the day at a summer wedding or garden party, use a powder finish. Loose powder is

a great way to 'set' make-up, but it can be tricky to apply if you're not used to it. Instead opt for a compact powder in a palette of toning shades and sweep a big brush over all the colours. Apply to forehead, chin, cheeks and nose – the mix of tones will give a luminous effect and the compact formula will avoid powder settling in creases and wrinkles.

DON'T QUOTE ME, BUT…
'I think being able to age gracefully is a very important talent. It is too late for me'
Clint Eastwood

ALL THINGS BRIGHT AND BEAUTIFUL
Common Blue butterfly
As you might expect, this is our commonest grassland butterfly. The males have bright blue wings with white margins; the females tend to be brown with a dusting of blue, but with the same white margins. They're on the wing from May to June; the second brood from late July to September. The caterpillars feed on birds-foot trefoil and clover. If you're interested in butterflies, join the Big Butterfly Count this month at www.bigbutterflycount.org/

DID YOU KNOW?

Stat attack

More than 2,500 left-handed people are killed every year, by using products made for right-handed people

An average person uses about 57 sheets of toilet paper a day

Camels can survive in a desert without drinking for almost 3 months

UNEXPECTED ANNIVERSARIES

I DON'T SEE THE PROBLEM

August 2014 is the 668th anniversary of:
the Battle of Crécy

Blind King John of Bohemia loved a fight even though, as his name hints, he was almost totally blind. At Crécy, he was supporting Philip VI of France against the English. With no way of knowing which way to ride or who to attack, he got two knights to tie their horses on either side of his and charged into battle that way *(see above)*.

He was killed, along with 30,000 allies, but his bravery did not go unremarked: legend says victorious Edward Prince of Wales, the Black Prince, took his motto *'Ich dien'* and the ostrich feathers from his helmet, and they remain the crest and motto of the Princes of Wales to this day.

WOTEVA!

Teenage translator

Meaty
Good. 'That track is meaty, dude.' Seldom applied to vegetarian dishes, however tasty. Teens tend not to do irony

Nut huggers
Very tight jeans, worn by men with very high voices

Zizou
To head-butt someone, a nod to the footballer, Zinedine Zidane

PET OF THE MONTH
The house rabbit

Name: Splodge
Owner's name: Katy Bravery
Best habit: Greeting his owner ecstatically on her arrival home
Worst habit: Being amorous with anything fluffy
Likes: Parsley and dandelion leaves
Dislikes: Cheap rabbit food
Personality: Proud, elegant, wild, elusive
Naughtiest moment: Breaking out of the house and eating most of a neighbour's tulips

TOP TECHIE TIP
Some day my prints will come

You'll probably have photos on your digital camera or smartphone that you'd like to turn into prints. How exactly do you this? Look for photo kiosks for digital media in some stores. Online, several photo-printing company names from the pre-digital era such as Truprint and Bonusprint offer a website service, along with a slew of new kids on the internet block, including Snapfish, Photobox and Pixum. You might be lucky enough to find an independent photo-printing service near you: look on www.ukcamera.com.

JOKE OF THE MONTH
Recent research has shown that six out of seven dwarves aren't happy.

sent in by Jonathan Beal

HOW TO MAKE A BAG-IN-A-BAG

Plastic carrier bags are a definite no-no for style and eco reasons. This homemade replacement is strong enough to carry lots of heavy groceries, light enough to fit in your handbag and über-stylish

YOU WILL NEED
1m (39in) in any standard width of strong fabric, but not too thick
Cotton thread for machine sewing
20–30cm (8–12in) ribbon
A pretty button

WHAT TO DO
1. To make the bag, cut out a rectangular piece of fabric measuring 80 x 46cm (32 x 18in). This includes a 1.5cm (½in) seam allowance.
2. To make the straps, cut two strips of fabric, each measuring 54 x 9cm (21 x 3½in). Fold in 5mm (¼in) on each side to the wrong side and iron flat. Fold each strap in half lengthways (so that the pattern is on the outside and the folded edges are inside), and machine topstitch all the way along.
3. For the top edge of the bag, fold in one of the longer sides of the fabric by 3mm (⅛in) to the wrong side.
4. Iron in place and then fold down a further 4cm (1½in) and iron again.
5. Pin the two handles in place. Pin one end of the first handle about 10cm (4in) in from the right-side edge, then pin the other end about 13cm (5in) away. Make sure the stitches on the handles face inward, and that the bottom of each handle is level with the bottom of the folded-over edge of the bag. Repeat at the opposite end (starting 10cm/4in in from the left-side edge) for handle two.
6. With the handles in place, stitch down the top of the bag with two rows of machine stitching, one about 3mm (⅛in) from the top edge and the other along the bottom of the folded-over edge.
7. Fold the bag in half, right sides together. Sew the side and bottom seams about 1.5cm (½in) in from the edge. Zigzag stitch over the raw edges to prevent fraying.
8. To make the gusset, open the bag out so the bottom seam runs down the centre and sew a diagonal line of about 10cm (4in) across each corner.
9. To make the ribbon and button tie, loop the length of ribbon around one of the handles, securing with a button.
10. To pack the bag, fold it into three sections and roll up, leaving the straps end until last. Then wrap the ribbon tie around the roll and wind the loose end of ribbon around the button.

USE IT OR LOSE IT
BRAIN EXERCISE
Give your grey matter a work-out

SUDOKU
The game of logic. Place each of the digits 1 to 9 in each row, column and 3x3 box. There is only one solution.

		4	7			1		8
9					7			
	1			8				
3			7	9			8	
2	7						9	5
	8			6	5			4
		1				3		
	4							1
6	9			8	2			

GRAMMAR CHALLENGE
The Lynne Truss test Can you spot the errors in grammar, punctuation and spelling? See below for the correct version.

i had a complicated fascinating six hour tutorial on the language people tend to use when they are lying and there was a tv camera in my face throughout key words or phrases or pausing in certain places gives liars away asked why should i believe you a truthful person might say because im telling the truth whereas the liar will say why should i lie or i don't know then theres lying by ommision liars tell the truth up to the point of the incident they want to hide skip that part then continue with the truth

AUGUST'S GENERAL KNOWLEDGE QUIZ
1 Which singer released the live album *Hot August Night* in 1972?
A. Barry Manilow, B. Frank Sinatra,
C. Neil Diamond, D. Bette Midler

2 To whom did President Richard Nixon address his resignation letter on August 9, 1974?
A. The Senate Leader, B. The Vice-President,
C. The Leader of Congress, D. The Secretary of State

3 'Men are my hobby, if I ever got married I'd have to give it up' is attributed to which Hollywood siren, (b. August 17, 1893)?
A. Louise Brooks, B. Mae West, C. Clara Bow, D. Lillian Gish

4 Which big band leader (b. August 1904) appeared in the comedy film *Blazing Saddles*?
A. Woody Herman, B. Duke Ellington,
C. Count Basie, D. Buddy Rich

5 Who succeeded Augustus Caesar as Roman Emperor in 14AD?
A. Tiberius, B. Claudius, C. Caligula, D. Nero

6 The triptych *Garden of Earthly Delights* by Hieronymous Bosch (d. August 9, 1518) is displayed in which museum?
A. The Louvre, B, Museo del Prado,
C. Pinacoteca di Brera, D. Rijksmuseum

7 Which rock act closed the Woodstock Festival in 1969?
A. The Who, B. Jefferson Airplane,
C. Jimi Hendrix, D. Ten Years After

8 What is the name of Sir Walter Scott's (b. August 1771) hero in *Ivanhoe*?
A. Wilfred, B. Brian, C. Geoffrey, D. Mark

9 In the 1967 FA Charity Shield, which goalkeeper scored against Manchester United?
A. Gordon Banks, B. Pat Jennings,
C. Gordon West, D. Bob Wilson?

10 In which county did the Great Train Robbery take place on August 8, 1963?
A. Buckinghamshire, B. Hertfordshire,
C. Bedfordshire, D. Oxfordshire

I had a complicated, fascinating six-hour tutorial on the language people tend to use when they are lying – and there was a TV camera in my face throughout. Key words or phrases, or pausing in certain places, give liars away. Asked: 'Why should I believe you?' a truthful person might say: 'Because I'm telling the truth,' whereas the liar will say: 'Why should I lie?' or 'I don't know'. Then there's lying by omission: liars tell the truth up to the point of the incident they want to hide, skip that part, then continue with the truth.

ANSWERS
1. C, 2. D,
3. B, 4. C,
5. A, 6. B,
7. C, 8. A,
9. B, 10. A

7	5	4	2	8	3	1	6	9
1	2	8	6	5	9	4	3	7
3	9	6	7	4	1	2	5	8
4	7	3	5	2	6	9	8	1
5	6	1	4	3	8	7	2	9
9	8	2	1	6	7	5	4	3
4	1	7	9	2	6	8	5	3
6	3	9	8	1	5	3	7	2
8	1	6	9	7	4	2	3	5

SEPTEMBER
2014

**MOMENT OF
REFLECTION**
Trebarwith Strand, Cornwall
Photograph by Saga Magazine
reader Geoffrey Massey

SEPTEMBER

1
Monday

2
Tuesday

3
Wednesday

4
Thursday

5
Friday

6
Saturday

7
Sunday

8
Monday

9
Tuesday

10
Wednesday
(event) **Art Late Turner: Painting Set Free**
Tate Britain, Millbank, London (to Jan 18, 2015)

11
Thursday

12
Friday

13
Saturday

14
Sunday

15
Monday

16
Tuesday

17
Wednesday

18
Thursday
(event) **Exhibition The Ming Dynasty**
British Museum, London (to April 4, 2015)

Saga Magazine has everything you need to fill your days

Diary looking a bit empty this month? Pick up your copy of Saga and turn to the Out There pages. Every month we give you details of events all over the country, from music festivals to literary get-togethers, celebratory anniversaries and days out. We review the latest films and give you the lowdown on what everyone's talking about – from plays, musicals and dance, to unmissable exhibitions. And you can find even more online at **www.saga.co.uk/magazine**. To subscribe call 0800 056 1057 or go to **www.saga.co.uk/magazine-subscriptions**

19
Friday

20
Saturday

21
Sunday

22
Monday

23
Tuesday

24
Wednesday

25
Thursday

26
Friday

27
Saturday
 **Gardening RHS Malvern Autumn Show**
Worcestershire (to Sept 28)

28
Sunday

29
Monday

30
Tuesday

DECADE BUSTERS

SEPTEMBER BIRTHDAYS

TURNING 70
Michael Douglas *American actor (right)*
Anne Robinson *TV presenter*
TURNING 60
Cherie Booth (Blair) QC *barrister*
Anne Diamond *TV presenter*

TURNING 50
Keanu Reeves *American actor*

THIS WEEK'S TOP TIP

Indoor hyacinths Plant specially treated bulbs now for flowers at Christmas

GARDENING

Set bulbs in pots with their tips above the level of the compost – don't mix different colours in one pot as they won't flower at the same time. You can use pretty bowls from junk shops: add a layer of broken-up polystyrene to the pots before you add the compost to act as a drainage layer.

Or look out for traditional Victorian glass bulb vases and grow hyacinths in water instead. Put a piece of artists' charcoal in the water to keep it sweet and fill the vase so that the base of the bulb sits fractionally above the water line.

Put the bulbs in a dark cupboard and keep the compost barely moist and the water in the vase topped up. Check weekly and bring the bulbs out into the light once you can see a hint of the flower head in the emerging leaves – usually by the beginning of December.

ALL THINGS BRIGHT AND BEAUTIFUL
Red admiral butterfly

The red admiral's name is a truncation of the original 18th-century 'red admirable'. These bold and beautiful butterflies migrate here every year from Europe – though there is evidence that some adults are managing to survive the winter in southern England. They lay their eggs on nettles, the caterpillars' food plant, and the first UK brood of butterflies are on the wing by late summer. In autumn look out for them on windfall apples or rotting blackberries.

RECIPE OF THE WEEK
Gloriously Nutty Soda Bread
Makes 1 large loaf (cuts into 10 slices)

Prepare 10 mins **Cook** 35-40 mins
250g (9oz) plain wholemeal flour, plus extra for dusting
250g (9oz) plain white flour
25g (1oz) essential Waitrose Butter
150g (5oz) Dorset Cereals Gloriously Nutty
25g (1oz) Waitrose Golden Caster Sugar
1½ tsp bicarbonate of soda
2 x 284ml cartons buttermilk

1 Preheat the oven to 190C/370F/gas 5. Place the flours in a large bowl then, using your fingertips, rub in the butter.
2 Stir in the Dorset Cereals Gloriously Nutty, sugar and bicarbonate of soda. Make a well in the centre, pour in the buttermilk and quickly bring together to make a very soft and sticky dough.
3 Tip the dough onto a heavily floured surface and, with dusted hands, pat the dough into a 20cm (8in) round. Transfer to a non-stick baking sheet and cut a deep cross in the top. Bake for 35-40 minutes until dark brown and completely cooked through. Transfer to a wire rack, cover with a clean tea towel and leave to cool before slicing.
Recipe and photograph from Waitrose. More than 5,000 recipes can be found at www.waitrose.com/recipes

DON'T QUOTE ME, BUT...
'I have yet to hear a man ask for advice on how to combine marriage and a career'
Gloria Steinem

'The disruption also brings unexpected romance'

The Bachelor
Stella Gibbons
(Vintage, £8.99)

The Blitz is at its height and London is in chaos, but siblings Constance and Kenneth Fielding try to preserve a life of calm. Their house in the suburbs is a haven of tranquillity. When a series of guests starts to arrive, peace is shattered. A Balkan exile, an old girlfriend and their own disreputable father all turn up at Sunglades and far outstay their welcome. But the domestic disruption also brings unexpected romance in its wake.

As chosen by the staff of Slightly Foxed bookshop, specialists in unusual titles, old and new; www.foxedbooks.com

Take a bow – or a violin

Fetch your childhood violin from the attic. It may be worth more than you think, as stringed instruments tend to rise in value with age

How many of us have given up the violin? Many parents were only too glad to consign the source of that dreaded racket to the attic. Now your instrument of torture may command a healthy price.

Of course, it's unlikely to be a 17th- or 18th-century Italian model, which would be worth hundreds of thousands of pounds or, in the case of a Stradivarius, a few million. But unlike many wind instruments, stringed instruments tend to rise in value. Indeed, quite ordinary models can fetch several hundred pounds.

Perhaps the most promising are those that have been handed down from generation to generation. Early violins by English makers such as Richard Duke and Benjamin Banks can fetch more than £10,000. But even a later model made in France, Germany or Japan may, nevertheless, have some value.

Sometimes a bow can be worth more than the instrument. The record is £101,000 for a bow by François Tourte of France. Bows from the English maker James Tubbs also sell for tens of thousands of pounds.

SOLD

This 18th-century Venetian cello fetched £121,250 at Bonhams in London in March, 2012

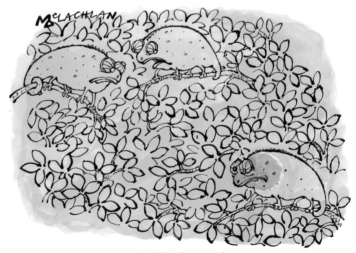

'High blood pressure.'

THIS WEEK'S TOP TIP
Exercise to help arthritis

HEALTH

When you're living with the pain of arthritis, exercise may well be the last thing on your mind. But research has proved that exercise can help limit pain, strengthen joints, improve mobility and boost your energy. The NHS recommends that people should exercise for 30 minutes a day: if that seems daunting, then try breaking it up into 10- or even 5-minute sessions.

Arthritis sufferers can benefit from three main types of exercise: range-of-movement exercises that build up the abilities of the joints; strengthening exercises that increase muscle strength; and aerobic exercise that raises your heart rate and burns off calories. Before you start, ask your GP or your physiotherapist to help you draw up a personalised exercise plan.

DON'T QUOTE ME, BUT...

'I hate housework! You make the beds, you do the dishes and six months later you have to start all over again'
Joan Rivers

ALL THINGS BRIGHT AND BEAUTIFUL
Goldfinches

Goldfinches are moving up the garden-bird league table as competition for food in the wider countryside increases. Seed-eating goldfinches feed on everything from dandelions to teasels – a great reason to grow the latter in your garden, even though they're rather invasive. Goldfinches are the only species that can successfully eat teasel seeds, as they have long slim beaks to extract the seeds from the prickly heads; they also seem to be able to cling on to them during strong winds. If you don't want to grow teasels, entice goldfinches into the garden with sunflower hearts or niger seed in your feeders instead.

RECIPE OF THE WEEK
Roquefort, Serrano Ham & Pear Salad
Serves 4 as a starter or light lunch

Prepare 10 mins
2 Waitrose Perfectly Ripe Pears, peeled, cored and sliced
Juice of 1 lemon
120g bag Waitrose Peppery Rocket Salad
70g pack Unearthed Spanish Serrano Ham
75g (3oz) Roquefort cheese, cubed
1 tbsp extra-virgin olive oil
2 tbsp natural yogurt
120g pack Waitrose Pomegranate Seeds

1 Toss the pear slices with half the lemon juice. Arrange the salad on four serving plates. On top, scatter the pear slices, slices of ham and the Roquefort.
2 Whisk together the remaining lemon juice, olive oil, yogurt and seasoning. Drizzle over the salad and scatter with the pomegranate seeds. Serve.
Recipe and photograph from Waitrose. More than 5,000 recipes can be found at www.waitrose.com/recipes

BADGER'S BLOG
'THEY WON'T PICK A FIGHT WITH A KILLING MACHINE'

Badger is on loan to the neighbours for a highly specialised operation

Word has got round that I'm a fearless ratter. The DFLs were boasting that we'd never had a rat in the garden (not alive, anyway). Well, of course we haven't, I make very sure of that. But at this time of year I've got my work cut out. They come in from the fields when the crops are harvested, and create new nests in gardens (or those gardens that don't have me on patrol). So Helen and Tony, the home providers for the Horrible H's, told GOB that they'd seen a 'monster' rat underneath their decking, along with evidence of some smaller ones.

Let's be honest, the neighbours have never been my biggest fans, but they had asked politely if they could borrow me for a highly specialist mission.

My immediate reaction was to ask why their useless flea-ridden furballs couldn't sort the problem out, but they quickly answered that by saying that the king rat was bigger than both of them. H&H had apparently taken refuge in the room above the garage and wouldn't come out.

So I went round and went through the motions of snarling at the garage, before setting to work around the decking. This involved a lot of sniffing, scratching and barking, and... er... leaving a scent. Rats aren't stupid (unlike Bob) and they're not cowards (unlike the Horrible H's), but they're sensible enough not to pick a fight with a highly efficient killing machine (viz. me).

Suffice it to say that the rats weren't seen again. I followed up with a morning and evening surveillance over the next week, and my mission was accomplished.

Name this month: *Rattus Invictus (that's more like it).*
Best moment: *Leaving something unpleasant for H&H outside their garage door.*

This is what I call multitasking – fetching a stick while keeping an eye out for rats

RECIPE OF THE WEEK
Root Vegetable Samosas with Mint Raita
Serves 4 (makes 12 samosas)

Prepare 15-20 mins **Cook** 15 mins
1 large carrot, trimmed and thickly sliced
1 small swede, peeled and cubed
1 parsnip, trimmed and thickly sliced
100g (3½oz) essential Waitrose Garden Peas (frozen)
3 tbsp groundnut oil
1 small onion, thinly sliced
2 cloves garlic, crushed
1-2 tbsp medium curry powder
1 tsp cumin seeds
28g pack fresh coriander, chopped
270g pack Jus-Rol Filo Sheets
4 tbsp essential Waitrose Natural Yogurt
2 tbsp essential Waitrose Mint Sauce

1 Preheat the oven to 200C/400F/gas 6. Cook the root vegetables in a pan of boiling water for 10 minutes until just cooked through. Drain, then cut into small cubes.
2 Cook the peas in boiling water for a minute and drain thoroughly. Heat half the oil in a frying pan and add the onion and garlic. Cook over a medium heat for 5 minutes until softened. Add the root vegetables and cook for a further couple of minutes. Stir in the spices and cook for a further minute. Stir in the peas, coriander and seasoning.
3 Brush a sheet of filo with oil, then fold in half. Cut in half across the diagonal to give two triangles. Place a large spoonful of the filling on one end of a triangle of pastry and fold over; keep folding until you have a triangular parcel. Pinch the edges together to seal. Repeat to make 12 samosas. Place on a dampened baking sheet and bake for 15 minutes. Serve with yogurt mixed with mint sauce.
Recipe and photograph from Waitrose. More than 5,000 recipes can be found at www.waitrose.com/recipes

THIS WEEK'S TOP TIP
Have you applied for Pension Credit?

MONEY
Pension credit is a way of topping up your income so that you have a guaranteed minimum to live on. It is means-tested on your savings and income, but don't let that put you off: even if you qualify for only the very minimum amount, the fact that you receive pension credit entitles you to other useful benefits such as help with health costs (for example, dental treatment or spectacles), council tax support and housing benefit. You can apply online at gov.uk or phone 0800 991234.

ALL THINGS BRIGHT AND BEAUTIFUL
Wood mouse
As autumn approaches, wood mice venture into gardens in search of food and shelter. These agile creatures will climb shrubs to get to berries and may also visit bird feeders for nuts and seeds, but are most commonly spotted foraging for berries and nuts underneath shrubs. Wood mice are easily distinguished from house mice by their chestnut brown fur on top and white tummies.

DON'T QUOTE ME, BUT...
'A man is a fool if he drinks before he reaches the age of 50, and a fool if he doesn't afterward'

Frank Lloyd Wright

EXTRACTED FROM *Tiny Islands* BY DIXE WILLS (AA PUBLISHING, £14.99)

TINY ISLANDS
LEFT TO THE BIRDS

The rocky prison that happily became
a wildlife sanctuary

BASS ROCK
Firth of Forth, off
North Berwick
Size: 7 acres
Population: 0

Bass Rock can honestly
claim to be one of the nation's
most important seven-acre
plots. In its time it has been home to
a hermitage, a chapel, a castle,
a feared prison and (inevitably)
a lighthouse. As if all this were not
enough, it has also been fêted by
none other than Sir David
Attenborough, who has called it 'one
of the 12 wildlife wonders of the world'.

Approach the island in summer and
you'd be forgiven for thinking that
your eyes are deceiving you, for
it appears to be entirely covered with
a light sprinkling of snow. It is when
the first volley of huge white seabirds
takes you by surprise by swooping
over your boat that the light dawns:
the 'snow' consists of thousands upon
thousands of northern gannets. At
the last count, there were 55,482 pairs
nesting, making the Bass Rock the
largest single-rock colony in the
known world.

And the closer you come, the more
extraordinary that home looks. Nests
cover the flat (well, flat-ish) heights,
the plunging slopes and, seemingly
impossibly, the precipitous cliffs. All
the while, restless clouds of gannets
hover above the island like midges

swarming over a Highland moor. Of
course, it wasn't always like this.

For centuries, local people used the
Bass Rock gannets as a source of
meat, oil, eggs (Queen Victoria was a
particular fan) and guano (but less a
fan of this). The Victorians, bless
them, sent men abseiling down the
cliffs on ropes to bludgeon the young
birds to death. The birds, generations
of which had been nesting there for
thousands of years, dwindled
dramatically in number. The slaughter
became one of the stimuli for the
passing of the enlightened Wild Birds
Protection Act of 1880, which was
successful in saving the colony.

Way back in the early 7th century,
an evangelist called Baldred had
founded a monastery at nearby
Tyninghame as part of his mission to
bring Christianity to the heathen East
Lothians. He then chose the Bass
Rock as an ideal place for a hermitage
where he could see out his final
years in peace (so one assumes there
were fewer gannets back then).

From 1671, Charles II used Bass
Rock as a state prison. And it was
as a prison that it entered its darkest
days. The Covenanters – Scottish
Presbyterians – were severely

persecuted by Charles II and about
40 or so of them found themselves
imprisoned there. Life was almost
intolerable. Prisoners had to rely on
friends and family to row across to
the island with provisions, or pay the
prison governor hugely inflated
prices. Water had to be lapped from
puddles and, should any prisoner
displease the governor, he was sent
down to the lowest cells where sea
spray soaked then froze him.

The prison had long fallen into ruin
when a juvenile Robert Louis
Stevenson spent several summer
holidays at a farm opposite. In his
novel *Catriona* he had his hero David
Balfour imprisoned there. The
Stevenson family connection with the
island was cemented in 1902 when
its lighthouse was built by Robert
Louis' cousins Charles and David. The
last keepers left in 1988 when it
was automated, since when the island
has been left to the birds.

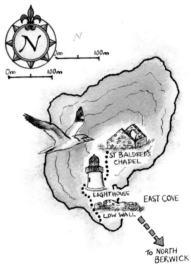

HOW TO GET THERE
Take the train to North Berwick. A trip
around Bass Rock is available from
the Scottish Seabird Centre from
March to October. Landing trips on
Bass Rock give 5½ hours on the island
but sail less frequently, run only
from April to September, and are
much more expensive.

RECIPE OF THE WEEK
Brown Sugar Plums with Soured Cream
Serves 4

Prepare 5 mins **Cook** 25 mins
8 essential Waitrose English Plums,
   halved and stoned
2 tbsp light brown muscovado sugar
½ tsp ground cinnamon
300ml (½ pint) essential Waitrose Soured Cream
2 tbsp demerara sugar

1. Heat the oven to 220C/425F/gas 7. Arrange the plums in a gratin dish to make a tight-fitting single layer. Mix together the brown sugar and cinnamon, and sprinkle over the plums. Bake for 20-25 minutes until the plums are tender and golden.
2. Spoon the soured cream over the top and sprinkle with the demerara sugar. For a crunchier sugar topping, you could place the dish under a hot grill until the sugar melts, but it's not essential. Serve with shortbread biscuits.
Recipe and photograph from Waitrose. More than 5,000 recipes can be found at www.waitrose.com/recipes

THIS WEEK'S TOP TIP
Get into handy habits

BEAUTY

Stock up on hand cream and keep a tube by all the washbasins in your home, as well as at work, in the car and even by the bed.
   Always apply hand cream before you pull on rubber gloves – the warmth of the washing-up water enhances the effect of the hand cream. And never go out in the garden without gardening gloves if you're the sort who's tempted to pull up a few weeds on the way to the shed.
   To improve fingertip circulation, try drumming your nails on your desk, table or worktop – but be warned, this may irritate anyone nearby.

ALL THINGS BRIGHT AND BEAUTIFUL
Tawny owl
The classic call of the tawny owl is the familiar 'tu-whit tu-whoo' – actually a duet between male and female. Pairs mate for life and stick to their established territory. The brood disperses from the nest in autumn and, at this time, both adults and fledglings call to establish and defend their patches with a whole range of sounds.

DON'T QUOTE ME, BUT...
'The face you have at age 25 is the face God gave you, but the face you have after 50 is the face you earned'
Cindy Crawford

UNEXPECTED ANNIVERSARIES
DOUBLE-DECKER LANDING
September 2014 is the 74th anniversary of:
the Brocklesby mid-air collision in Australia

In 1940, two Avro Ansons collided over Brocklesby in New South Wales and got stuck together, one on top of the other (*pictured above and below*). Three of the four crew members bailed out, but the pilot of the one on top (22-year-old Leonard Fuller) found that he was able to use the ailerons and flaps on his plane, combined with the engines on the one underneath, to control the flight and land both planes. Nobody was injured, and both the Ansons were eventually repaired and returned to service. Ironically, for somebody who had survived such an event, Fuller died in 1944 when his bicycle collided with a bus.

AUSTRALIAN WAR MEMORIAL

'I live here, but I forgot my key.'

WOTEVA!
Teenage translator

Cold finger
Not unlike 'cold shoulder', but when giving the cold finger, you ignore someone's text or Facebook message. Reserve the cold finger for the most pointless of texts

Cyber hoarding
Someone who keeps far too much stuff on their computer – things they will probably never look at again

Emotional dump
Unloading all your troubles at once on to an unsuspecting friend

Hype aversion
Rejecting something that is popular, just because it is popular. 'That film was out years ago, dude!' 'I know, but I only just got around to seein' it – I got hype aversion, dude...'

PET OF THE MONTH
No flies on me

Name: Charlestown Symphonic (Nicky)
Owner's name: Nicky owns Jane
Best habit: Being so fabulously
beautiful he makes you feel great
Worst habit: Giving appreciative
slobbery snuffles on your sleeves
Likes: Showing off to mares
Dislikes: Wearing wussy fly masks, bits
of which are strewn around his field
Personality: Kind and loving
Naughtiest moment: Those fly
masks, let me see, at £20 a pop...
Most human trait: Scared of things he
thinks could be dangerous: wolf-
shaped snow drifts; silently fast
cyclists (why no sound of hooves?)

TOP TECHIE TIP
Show me the money

Lots of mobile smartphone apps can
save you money – many are free.
Here are a couple of good ones.
Frustrated paying for 0800 calls on
your mobile when you have free
minutes with your phone plan? The
0800 Wizard app lets you call
freephone numbers free (for Android,
iPhone, Blackberry and Windows
phones). Saving for a holiday? Set
a goal on the OrSaveit app (for
iPhone). Every time you opt to save
rather than spend, add the money to
your account and watch it grow.

JOKE OF THE MONTH
**Two friends are chatting in the pub.
Tom: 'I had this delicious Chicken
Tarka for supper last night.'
Bill: 'Don't you mean Chicken Tikka?'
Tom: 'No. It's like Chicken
Tikka, but 'otter.'
sent in by Hazel Cooper**

HOW TO MAKE
A CROCHETED iPAD COVER

**This is a great, practical way to
make your iPad unique and its
simple shape means it is easy to
adapt for any tablet or e-reader.
The envelope-style button flap
stops the gadget from falling out**

YOU WILL NEED
*100g (3½ oz) double knit (DK)
   cotton yarn
3.5mm crochet hook
1 button
Darning needle*
ABBREVIATIONS
ch *chain,* **dc** *double crochet,* * *repeat*
sl st *slip stitch,* **sp** *space,* **tr** *treble*

TO MAKE
Make 33ch then turn. **Base row:** Work
1tr into 4th chain from hook, then 1tr
into all subsequent chain to end
(30sts). Make 3 turning ch, then turn.
Row 1: Work 1tr in every stitch to end
of row. Make 3 turning ch.* Repeat Row
1 until the work measures 50cm (19½in).
Next row: Tr next 2 sts together, work
to last 2 sts, tr next 2 sts together,

make 3 turning ch. Repeat last row
another 7 times.

TO MAKE UP
1 Fold your work in half, lining up the
base row with the last row made
before decreasing and pin in place.
2 Beginning at the bottom right-hand
corner, join your work together by
working a row of dc up the first seam,
around the envelope flap, and down
the second seam to the bottom
left-hand corner.
3 Make 2ch, turn, then make another
row of dc around your work. Break off
the yarn, thread it through the last
loop and sew in any loose ends.

TO MAKE THE BUTTON LOOP
4 Use a DK thread double (2 ends of
DK), make a foundation chain that will
fit around your chosen button – ours
was 10ch for a 2cm (¾in) button.
5 Sew both ends to the centre of the
envelope flap using a darning needle.
6 Using the same yarn and darning
needle, sew a button onto the case.

BRAIN EXERCISES
Give your grey matter a work-out

SUDOKU
The game of logic. Place each of the digits 1 to 9 in each row, column and 3x3 box. There is only one solution.

			3					
1			2				7	4
9	5					1		
	2	6		4	3			
		8		6		4		
		8	2		9	6		
	8						3	9
4	3			5				1
			8					

GRAMMAR CHALLENGE
The Lynne Truss test Can you spot the errors in grammar, punctuation and spelling? See below for the correct version.

i have definitely grown tidier with age in fact i have reached a good stage in life a sort of blessed equilibrium where i still like getting things out but i also like putting them back again as a young person you see i generally preferred getting them out i do hope no one ever reads this sentence out of context by the way as i get older i definately prefer putting away in my youth id make some tea and leave the mug under a pile of papers for days now i drink the tea wash the cup and put it back in the cupboard

SEPTEMBER'S GENERAL KNOWLEDGE QUIZ

1. Which Viking leader did King Harold defeat at the Battle of Stamford Bridge on September 25, 1066?
A. Erik Bloodaxe, B. Harald Hadrada,
C. Magnus Barefoot, D. Sweyn Esthrinson

2. September 19 marks which international event?
A. Talk Like a Pirate Day, B. Talk Like a Comedy Frenchman Day, C. Talk Like Homer Simpson Day,
D. Talk Like Marilyn Monroe Day

3. Who was British Foreign Secretary in September 1939?
A. Lord Chelmsford, B. Lord Strathclyde,
C. Viscount Halifax, D. Lord Salisbury

4 Who had a UK top three chart hit in 1978 with *September*?
A. KC and the Sunshine Band, B. Earth Wind and Fire,
C. Donna Summer, D. The Jacksons

5 *EastEnders* **star Jessie Wallace (b. September 21, 1971) played which iconic soap actress in the 2010 BBC drama** *The Road to Coronation Street*?
A. Doris Speed, B. Violet Carson,
C. Pat Phoenix, D. Julie Goodyear

6 In September 1899, French army officer Albert Dreyfus was released from the notorious penal colony of Devil's Island. Where was it located?
A. Guadeloupe, B, Haiti, C. French Guiana, D. Madagascar

7 Edgar Rice Burroughs created which fictional hero?
A. Tarzan, B. Superman, C. Biggles, D. Allan Quatermain

8 Which composer, (b. September 1, 1854) wrote the opera *Hansel and Gretel*?
A. Wilhelm Berger, B. Engelbert Humperdinck,
C. Carl Haupt, D. Richard Hofmann

9 What first lit up the sky in September 1879?
A. Blackpool Illuminations, B. Copenhagen's Tivoli Gardens,
C. Coney Island's Luna Park, D. Margate's Dreamland

10 Who was pronounced Lord Protector in September 1658?
A. Thomas Fairfax, B. Richard Cromwell,
C. Henry Ireton, D. George Monck

I have definitely grown tidier with age. In fact, I have reached a good stage in life – a sort of blessed equilibrium – where i still like getting things out, but I also like putting them back again. As a young person, you see, I generally preferred getting them out (I do hope no one ever reads this sentence out of context, by the way). As I get older, I definitely prefer putting away. In my youth, I'd make some tea and leave the mug under a pile of papers for days; now I drink the tea, wash the cup and put it back in the cupboard.

5	4	7	2	8	3	9	1	6
1	8	2	5	9	6	7	3	4
3	6	9	4	1	7	5	8	2
5	4	9	6	7	8	2	1	3
7	2	4	1	6	5	8	9	3
8	5	1	3	4	9	6	2	7
6	1	3	8	2	4	7	5	9
4	7	8	9	5	2	3	6	1
2	9	5	6	3	1	4	7	8

ANSWERS
1. B, 2. A
3. C, 4. B
5. C, 6. C
7. A, 8. B
9. A, 10.B

TAORMINA

In Taormina, spring starts in February and the sun shines until the end of October. With spectacular scenery and architecture, plus sweeping beaches, it's no surprise that this Sicilian gem has been a popular holiday destination for centuries

FIVE Q&AS

Where is Taormina?
On Mount Tauro, on the east coast of Sicily. The two-mile wide Strait of Messina divides Sicily from mainland southern Italy.

When should I go? Taormina enjoys a mild climate all year round. Spring is the best time to visit: it begins in February when almond trees blossom and temperatures stay comfortable into May and June. From May to October the temperatures average 24-32C. Winter lasts for just two months, there is never a frost and the only snow you'll see will be on Mount Etna's summit.

Will I see any celebs? Taormina has always attracted the elite since it became part of the European Grand Tour back in the 17th century. Big names in the 20th century included D H Lawrence, Truman Capote and Cary Grant. These days, Madonna has rented a property and singer Mick Hucknall has a vineyard on the slopes of Etna, while Gerard Depardieu and Georgio Armani have estates on nearby islands.

By April, hills and terraces are clothed in the yellow of broom and mimosa

Any bright lights? Definitely. There are dozens of bars, restaurants and chic boutiques in Corso Umberto, the pedestrianised main thoroughfare. When eating out, try *arancini*, deep-fried risotto balls.

How do I get there? Catania, on Sicily's eastern coast, is the closest airport. There is a new cruise port at Messina, where many passengers hop off for a tour of Taormina.

There has long been talk of a bridge to join Sicily to mainland Italy, across the Strait of Messina but the political promises seem to get forgotten.

If you are driving to Taormina, be aware that most of the town's narrow streets are closed to traffic, but there is plenty of parking in the lower area of the town.

FOUR SIGHTS TO SEE

Mount Etna, at 11,000ft is Europe's largest and one of the most active volcanoes and is an hour's drive away.

The town is a mixture of Norman, baroque and Gothic architecture

Walk in Michael Corleone's footsteps. Francis Ford Coppola filmed all of *The Godfather* trilogy's Sicilian scenes near Taormina. Hire a vintage Fiat 500 and follow a tour guide to the hillside villages.

Casa Cuseni. The villa was left to young Englishwoman Daphne Phelps by her uncle. She travelled to Sicily in 1947 to sell the property but fell in love with it and never returned to England. She lived in the villa until she died in 2005.

It is now an Italian National Monument, museum and B&B. The villa is full of arts including a Frank Brangwyn mural, ancient Islamic ceramics, a Picasso ink drawing and letters from Tennessee Williams.

Castelmola, a pretty village perched 1,000ft above Taormina. Keen walkers can take the path to the small square. Have a breather while leaning on the balcony and enjoy the view of Etna.

THREE THINGS TO KNOW

The English garden in Taormina was created by Lady Florence Trevelyan. In 1884, she was 'invited' to leave England within 48 hours when Queen Victoria realised she was falling in love with the future king, Edward, who was married to Alessandra of Denmark.

Aged 27, Florence found herself in perpetual exile. After more than two years' travelling, she settled in Taormina. Florence fell in love again, this time with the town's mayor.

The wealthy couple bought 70 acres on the edge of Taormina and set about creating the garden, which is now a public amenity.

Spring comes early. Wisteria blossoms in February. By April, the hills and terraces are clothed in yellow as broom, mimosa, euphorbia and cat's claw cascade from walls. In May, gardens turn pink, purple and red

TAORMINA, SICILY
LAT. 38°N
LONG. 14°E

Mount Etna in spring, framed with a border of bright yellow broom

as hibiscus, bougainvillea and geraniums come into flower.

Taormina is 800ft above sea level but it is easy to get to the beaches: it takes just three minutes by cable car.

TWO THINGS TO AVOID

August. It can be really hot when the sirocco brings temperatures of 43-45C.

Hairpin bends. If you are not a keen driver, join a tour or hire a cab and let local drivers negotiate the roads.

ONE MUST-DO

Visit Teatro Antico di Taormina, the ancient Greek theatre. Mount Etna and the sea provide the most dramatic backdrop. Built into the rock during the third century BC, almost 5,000 seats were cut into the stone. Some still survive.

In the second century AD, the Romans transformed the site into an amphitheatre. They took down the stage and were much more interested in gladiatorial battles and lion-fighting. Nowadays, a stage is erected for outdoor shows from May to September, with productions ranging from opera, ballet and concerts to Shakespeare.

Taormina has long been popular with artists, intellectuals and film stars

Does Saga go there?
Yes, find out more about travel to Sicily at saga.co.uk/sicily

OCTOBER
2014

THE OLD BEECH
Forest of Dean, Gloucestershire
Photograph by Saga Magazine
reader Michael Bramwell

OCTOBER

1
Wednesday

2
Thursday

3
Friday

4
Saturday

5
Sunday

6
Monday

7
Tuesday

8
Wednesday

9
Thursday

10
Friday

11
Saturday

12
Sunday

13
Monday

14
Tuesday

15
Wednesday

16
Thursday

17
Friday

18
Saturday

Saga Magazine has everything you need to fill your days

Diary looking a bit empty this month? Pick up your copy of Saga and turn to the Out There pages.
Every month we give you details of events all over the country, from music festivals to literary
get-togethers, celebratory anniversaries and days out. We review the latest films and give you the lowdown
on what everyone's talking about – from plays, musicals and dance, to unmissable exhibitions.
And you can find even more online at **www.saga.co.uk/magazine**. To subscribe call 0800 056 1057
or go to **www.saga.co.uk/magazine-subscriptions**

19
Sunday

20
Monday

21
Tuesday

22
Wednesday

23
Thursday

24
Friday

25
Saturday

26
Sunday
British Summer Time ends

27
Monday

28
Tuesday

29
Wednesday

30
Thursday

31
Friday
Halloween

DECADE BUSTERS

OCTOBER BIRTHDAYS

TURNING 70
Mandy Rice-Davies *former model and showgirl*
Angela Rippon *(right) TV presenter*
TURNING 60
Mario Testino *photographer*

TURNING 50
Yasmin Le Bon *model*
Harry Hill *comedian*
Clive Owen *actor*

REX

THIS WEEK'S TOP TIP
How to plant a tree

GARDENING
Autumn is ideal for planting bare-root or container-grown trees: the soil is still warm and moist, giving the trees a chance to get established before winter sets in.

Start by ridding the soil of weeds – try to dig these out from the base of a young tree and you risk damaging its roots. Dig a hole slightly deeper than the container or the roots of the tree. Fork over the base of the hole to improve drainage. Hammer in a stake before you plant the tree, to avoid damaging its roots. Plant the tree at the same depth it was growing in the container – or in the field in the case of a bare-root tree – you'll see a clear line on the trunk with the latter.

Mix a handful of bonemeal or fertiliser with the soil from the hole and refill it, firming the soil gently as you go. Water well and continue to water the tree regularly for the first year or so.

RECIPE OF THE WEEK
Baked Pumpkin Gratin with Rosemary & Goat's Cheese
Serves 4

Prepare 15 mins **Cook** 1 hour
900g (2lb) Waitrose Small Pumpkin, peeled, deseeded and cubed (or 1 large butternut squash)
2 cloves garlic, roughly chopped
2 tbsp fresh rosemary, chopped
1 tsp cumin seeds
300ml (½ pint) vegetable stock (or white wine)
150ml (¼ pint) essential Waitrose Single Cream
25g (1oz) pumpkin seeds
25g (1oz) white breadcrumbs
50g (2oz) mild goat's cheese, grated

1. Preheat the oven to 180C/350F/gas 4. Place the pumpkin or squash in a shallow 2 litre (3½ pint) ovenproof dish or roasting tin. Scatter the garlic, rosemary, cumin and seasoning on top. Pour in the stock and bake for 40-45 minutes until the squash is almost tender.
2. Increase the oven temperature to 200C/400F/gas 6. Pour the cream over the pumpkin and scatter with the pumpkin seeds, breadcrumbs and goat's cheese. Return to the oven for a further 12-15 minutes until the top is bubbling and golden. Serve with a green salad and crusty bread.
Recipe and photograph from Waitrose. More than 5,000 recipes can be found at www.waitrose.com/recipes

ALL THINGS BRIGHT AND BEAUTIFUL
Ivy flowers
Late-flowering ivy is one of the last, most important nectar sources for bees to stock the hive before winter and for late-flying butterflies before they hibernate. This plant tends to divide people into two camps: those who see it as a valuable wildlife habitat providing shelter, nesting sites and food; and those who see it as a destructive force, bringing down trees and walls by its great weight.

DON'T QUOTE ME, BUT...
'Whenever you find yourself on the side of the majority, it is time to pause and reflect'
Mark Twain

REDISCOVERED BOOK

A window into a world of street fairs and horse-drawn carts

Lifting the Latch
Sheila Stewart
(Day Books, £8.99)

For 80 years Montague 'Mont' Abbott of Enstone worked as a rural labourer in Oxfordshire, only once travelling further than seven miles from his birthplace to visit his brother in London. *Lifting the Latch* is his lyrical and unsentimental memoir, compiled from interviews by Sheila Stewart. She allows him to tell his story in his own words, including his stoical refrain, 'Us got over it'. A delightful window into an earlier pastoral world of street fairs, horse-drawn carts and roly-poly puddings.

As chosen by the staff of Slightly Foxed bookshop, specialists in unusual titles, old and new; www.foxedbooks.com

HIDDEN TREASURES
More than just a cuddly toy

Dust off your old teddies and check for any labels: if you are lucky enough to have been bought a Steiff as a child, you could be hugging a small fortune

It's widely known that teddy bears were named after Theodore Roosevelt and should on no account be chucked away if made by a German company called Steiff. The current record for a Steiff is £130,000, although they are usually worth far less than that, especially if missing the trademark button in the ear. The first teddy was made around 1902 and their popularity remains undimmed.

The oldest are generally the most valuable and although Steiff is king, those made by less well-known firms can fetch hefty prices. The German companies Bing, Clemens and Schuco are worth looking out for while Ideal in the USA was as much a pioneer as Steiff. Among the British companies Farnell, Chad Valley, Chiltern and Merrythought rate a mention.

SOLD
This rather dangerous Steiff hot-water bottle bear sold at Christie's, London, for £18,750 in October 2010

The bear should be made of mohair rather than synthetic fur and any receipts or documents you have relating to its history can add value. If, by some miracle, it's still in its original box, you can add another 10%. Most of the above mentioned companies made other types of cuddly toys, which can also attract high prices.

'And do you, Arnold Perkins, ignoring all advice from family and friends, take this woman to be...'

THIS WEEK'S TOP TIP
My head hurts

HEALTH

Regularly taking painkillers for a headache could be the reason your head hurts in the first place. More than a million people in the UK suffer from headaches caused by medication overuse, according to the National Institute for Health and Clinical Excellence (NICE). It's unclear exactly why – the medication seems to disrupt the balance of the body's pain control system. The treatment is to go 'cold turkey' and stop all painkillers, but see your GP first, of course.

RECIPE OF THE WEEK
Roasted Autumn Vegetables with Halloumi Cheese
Serves: 4

Preparation 15 mins **Cooking** 1 hour 10 mins

1 medium butternut squash
180g pack Romano peppers
2 red onions, peeled
4 tbsp olive oil
2 tbsp balsamic vinegar
250g pack Cypressa Cyprus Halloumi cheese, cut or torn into chunks
2 tbsp toasted pine nuts
Fresh basil leaves to garnish

1. Preheat the oven to 200C/400F/gas 6. Peel the squash, cut in half lengthways and remove the seeds. Cut the flesh into chunks and place in a large roasting tin. The vegetables generate a lot of steam, so use the biggest roasting tin you can.
2. Cut the peppers in half, remove the seeds and stalks, and cut into chunky pieces. Add them to the roasting tin. Halve the onions, then cut into small wedges and place in the tin. Drizzle the vegetables with the olive oil and coat well. Season with freshly ground black pepper. Roast in the oven for 45 minutes or until slightly charred at the edges.
3. Remove the vegetables from the oven and sprinkle with the vinegar. Scatter the cheese over the top and cook for a further 25 minutes or until the halloumi is golden.
4. Scatter the pine nuts and basil leaves over the top and serve piping hot.
Recipe and photograph from Waitrose. More than 5,000 recipes can be found at www.waitrose.com/recipes

ALL THINGS BRIGHT AND BEAUTIFUL
Giant puffball
This extraordinary mushroom can be the size of a football and can appear almost overnight in fields, hedgerows, on woodland margins and occasionally in gardens. There is nothing to mistake this edible mushroom for – it's a safe bet to identify. If you are going to cook it, peel it first and slice it into thick steaks. The flesh should be white: if it's yellowy or grey, then the puffball is past its best and not worth bothering with. Try frying slices in olive oil with garlic.

DON'T QUOTE ME, BUT...
'I think age is a very high price to pay for maturity'

Tom Stoppard

*'Egrets? I've had a few, but then again,
too few to mention.'*

BADGER'S BLOG

'BRIGHT, CRISP DAYS WHEN I DON'T ACTUALLY HAVE TO NAG TO BE TAKEN OUT FOR A WALK'

Badger explains why she's very fond of autumn

My favourite time of year!
Even though there are
no 'special' days, every
day is special. It's generally damp and
dank, and I can occupy that space
exclusively reserved for dogs right in
front of the fire. But there are also
bright, crisp autumn days when I don't
actually have to nag to be taken out,
and we spend a lot of time crunching
through leaves and having lunch in
pubs, where there are more interesting
smells than in any other human
habitat I've yet come across – not to
mention interesting scraps under
the tables. Like pork scratchings.

We also like hiring a motorhome
and doing a tour of our family and
friends (and their dogs), who we don't
often see for the rest of the year. BOG
and GOB have got this theory that
they'll actually be welcomed, even if
they turn up with me, if they bring
their own accommodation. That's why
they bought Myrtle the caravan in
the end, although she turned out to be
riddled with damp (I can't see why

that's a problem) but BOG doesn't
like to talk about it. For some reason
GOB likes to talk about it a lot.

But the best part of October is
when the smaller humans in the
village celebrate something called
Halloween and come round to
the front door dressed up as
monsters. BOG seems to get a lot of
pleasure out of getting me to wear
a special flashing collar, and sending
me round the side of the house
to greet them with the usual frenzy of
barking I reserve for all visitors.

For some reason there's always
a lot of screaming when I arrive low
and hard out of the darkness, and
BOG has been known to howl with
laughter as he stands at the front
door wearing something called
a Frankenstein mask.

Name this month: *Badgenstein.*
(This has got to stop.)
Best moment: *I ate an entire bag of
pork scratchings that somebody had
foolishly left within jaws distance.*

'Let me up there
too, please!'

THIS WEEK'S TOP TIP
Have you planned for the future?

MONEY

Research has shown that the average length of retirement in the UK is roughly 19 years, but the same study showed that the average Brit will have used up their retirement savings after just a third of that time. Of the 15 countries surveyed, Malaysia came out top: retirees there have sufficient funding to see them through 12 of their 17 years of retirement.

ALL THINGS BRIGHT AND BEAUTIFUL
Jay

Squirrels aren't the only creatures that store supplies for winter. Jays are fond of acorns and will travel up to four kilometres (2½ miles) in search of them, their throats expanding to carry a half-swallowed load of up to nine at a time. They bury the acorns for later in the winter – one jay may bury 3,000 in a month – and are good at remembering where they've hidden them. Those that they forget help in the distribution of oak trees.

DON'T QUOTE ME, BUT...

'When I was a boy the Dead Sea was only sick'

George Burns

RECIPE OF THE WEEK
Upside-down Pear Cake
Serves 8–10

Prepare 15 mins **Cook** 45-50 mins
200g (7oz) butter, softened
75g (3oz) light brown soft sugar
6 tbsp Chambord Black Raspberry Liqueur
4 Conference pears, peeled, halved and cored
175g (6oz) golden caster sugar
200g (7oz) self-raising flour
3 medium eggs, beaten
4 tbsp milk
Custard, to serve

1. Heat the oven to 170C/325F/gas 3. Mash together 50g (2oz) of the butter and all the brown sugar, then mix in 4 tbsp of the Chambord. Spread into the base of a deep, 23cm (9in) non-stick cake tin and place on a baking tray. Press the pears, cut-side down, into the mixture.
2. Using an electric whisk, beat together the golden caster sugar, remaining butter, flour, eggs and milk until well blended.
3. Spread over the pears and bake for 45-50 minutes until risen and firm to the touch. Leave to cool in the tin for 5 minutes, then turn out. Drizzle over the remaining 2 tbsp Chambord, then slice and serve warm with custard.
Recipe and photograph from Waitrose. More than 5,000 recipes can be found at www.waitrose.com/recipes

TIDE WAITS FOR NO MAN

Not even Dylan Thomas, who was stranded here

WORM'S HEAD
Nr Rhossili, Gower Peninsula, Swansea
Size: c. 33 acres
Population: 0

The English language is an incorrigible thief but sometimes its sins do find it out. Such is the case with Worm's Head, an extraordinary tidal island whose constituent parts bear little resemblance to any section of a worm (though, let's face it, all the sections of a worm look alike anyway, probably even to other worms).

They do, however, call to mind the top of a scaly dragon's neck and head. It's no surprise to learn, then, that the worm in this case is a corruption of the Old English *wyrm* – meaning dragon – which was probably stolen from the Old High German *wurm* or the Old Norse *ormr* or both. A mile-long rollercoaster jutting out into the Bristol Channel, it's one of Britain's most visually impressive chunks of landscape.

It's a gentle walk from the village of Rhossili along the coast to the Old Coastguard Lookout, now staffed by volunteers belonging to Coastwatch and it's immediately apparent why their presence is a good thing. The causeway far below is a long and jagged one and strandings are fairly common occurrences, despite their best efforts. A large

board displays the safe crossing times and there's a siren that can be sounded to warn stragglers.

There's no track across the wide curved causeway, so visitors must scramble over the rocks. At first there are mussels underfoot, then a variety of smaller crustaceans, then finally a whole new landscape complete with miniature rift valleys and lochs. It takes around 15 minutes if you don't dawdle.

On the far side is the largest hump of the island, the Inner Head, on

whose 150ft ridge an ancient promontory fort once stood. It was on the slopes of the Inner Head that a young Dylan Thomas fell asleep, missed the tide and had to wait until the next one, fortified only by a bag of sandwiches and a book.

He later recalled: 'I stayed on that Worm from dusk to midnight, sitting on that top grass, frightened to go further in because of the rats and because of things I am ashamed to be frightened of. Then the tips of the reef began to poke out of the water and, perilously, I climbed along them to the shore.'

The Worm's Head featured in Thomas' short story *Who Do You Wish Was With Us?*, which described a rather happier visit: 'The sea was out. We crossed over on slipping stones and stood, at last, triumphantly on the windy top. There was monstrous, thick grass there that made us spring-heeled and we laughed and bounced on it, scaring the sheep who ran up and down the battered sides like goats. Even on this calmest day a wind blew on the Worm.'

HOW TO GET THERE

Take the train to Swansea, then the no 118 bus across the Gower Peninsula to Rhossili. Passing the National Trust shop, there's a mile-long track to the coastal lookout that marks the start of the walk down the cliffs and across the rocks to Worm's Head. The island is usually accessible for around four to five hours at each low tide.

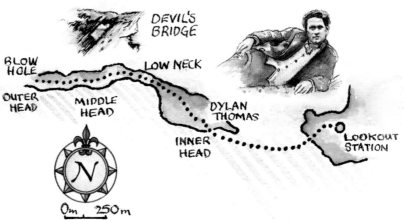

RECIPE OF THE WEEK
Sautéed Chicken with Cider & Tarragon
Serves 4

Prepare 20 mins **Cook** 50 mins

500ml bottle Waitrose Leckford Farm Cox's
   Apple Vintage Cider
8 essential Waitrose British Chicken Thigh Fillets
2 tsp Bart Ground Allspice
40g (1½oz) butter
2 Cox's apples, cored and cut into wedges
250g pack essential Waitrose Mushrooms,
   washed and sliced
15g pack fresh tarragon, finely shredded
4 tbsp double cream

1. Place the cider in a saucepan, bring to the boil and simmer until reduced by half.
2. Rub the chicken thighs on both sides with the allspice and a little salt.
3. Melt half the butter in a large, deep-sided frying pan or sauté pan with lid, and fry the apple wedges and mushrooms until golden. Drain with a slotted spoon and place on a plate. Keep warm.
4. Melt the remaining butter in the pan and fry the chicken pieces, in batches if necessary, until lightly browned. Pour in the reduced cider and bring to the boil. Reduce the heat and cook gently, covered, for 20-25 minutes, or until the chicken is thoroughly cooked.
5. Return the apples and mushrooms to the pan with the tarragon and cream. Season to taste and heat gently for 5 minutes, before serving with piping hot mashed potato.
Recipe and photograph from Waitrose. More than 5,000 recipes can be found at www.waitrose.com/recipes

BEAUTY

Start by looking after your teeth – the underlying structure of your face can have a big effect on your appearance. Drink plenty of water to keep your skin plump and hydrated. Exercise regularly to improve circulation, which will show on your face.

Always wear sunscreen when you go out – many moisturisers now have an SPF rating. Try taking a flaxseed oil supplement: it's a rich vegetable source of omega-3 fatty acids, which are vital for supple skin. And if you haven't already done so, give up smoking.

DON'T QUOTE ME, BUT...
'I have the body of an 18-year-old. I keep it in the fridge'
Spike Milligan

ALL THINGS BRIGHT AND BEAUTIFUL
Conkers
In the dim, distant past the game of conkers was played with snail shells or hazel nuts until the horse chestnut became established in Britain. By the 20th century, horse chestnuts were the weapon of choice, with a hole bored through the centre and threaded on a knotted string. All sorts of 'improvements' have been tried, from baking the conker in the oven, to boiling it in vinegar or salt water – methods that are banned in professional competitions.

'I'll have the happy meal.'

UNEXPECTED ANNIVERSARIES
THE ASCENT OF MAN

**October 2014 is the 13th anniversary of:
Ian Ashpole's record-setting rise to 11,000ft,
carried aloft by party balloons**

Mr Ashpole, from Herefordshire, rose to 5,000ft using
a support balloon (so that he'd have enough height to
parachute down if anything went wrong), but was lifted the
rest of the way by 600 helium-filled party balloons –
just like the film *Up* – before cutting himself loose and
parachuting to the ground.

The use of helium to fill party balloons is controversial
because, despite being very abundant in the universe
in general, helium is very rare on earth – for the obvious
reason that it all floats away into space. It's needed
for things such as cooling MRI scanners, so scientists feel
that it shouldn't be wasted on such frivolities.

WOTEVA!
Teenage translator

Du
More truncation, from txt spk wrld.
This time: 'Do you'. End it with a '?'
and you have a whole sentence in
two letters. Most teens would
consider that to be a strike. Du?

Quackpot
Somebody who claims expertise that
they do not possess, especially in
matters medical. 'Dat Minister for
Health dude – man, 'e is a quackpot'

Untopia
A living hell, the opposite of Utopia.
Actually, I think they mean
dystopia, but try telling a teen that

PET OF THE MONTH
Looking worried

Name: Rosie
Owner's name: Rosie owns Elizabeth
Best habit: Looking incredibly sweet
Worst habit: Dead-legging you in the
back of the knee with two front paws
Likes: Snuggling into a cosy blanket,
chasing foxes and squirrels
Dislikes: Being forced to go outside in
even mildly inclement weather to pee
Personality: Jolly, loyal, fierce
Naughtiest moment: Can't you see
the halo? But, wait, there was a
hairbrush that got reshaped recently...
Most human trait: Worrying about
Elizabeth when she goes away

TOP TECHIE TIP
I'll pass on that

Few of us would leave the house
without locking the door. Yet millions
of us use passwords on the internet
that are far too easy to crack. Once
you've settled on a tough password,
here's a tip: try Googling it. If the
word doesn't come up in your search,
there's a chance that it's never been
written down or said – that's good.
The strongpasswordgenerator.com
website will also conjure up
something likely to be unique to you.
But be warned: these passwords in
themselves can be hard to remember.

JOKE OF THE MONTH
Three elderly chaps were playing golf.
Jack: 'Windy, isn't it lads?'
Pete: 'It's Thursday.'
Alf: 'Me too, let's go for a beer.'

sent in by May McCahy

HOW TO MAKE
SPOOKY SILHOUETTES

**Spooky silhouettes and scary
shadows are synonymous with
October 31, and they're very
quick and easy to make. Choose
from witches, skeletons, cauldrons,
cats, bats or spiders to create
that suitably creepy atmosphere**

YOU WILL NEED
Craft knife
Pencil
Thin black card, sugar paper or similar
Sticky, reusable putty (such as
    Blu-tack™) for attaching silhouettes

TO MAKE
1. Measure the windows you want to
decorate, then cut your card to size.
2. If you don't feel confident in your
drawing abilities, search the web for
ideas. You can scale images up or
down on a photocopier.
3. On a piece of plain paper, sketch
where you want to place each image
(that way you won't run out of space).
4. Draw your images on to the card,
then carefully cut out the shape with

a craft knife. Remember that you are
cutting an outline only. You can stick
small detail pieces such as eyes in
position on the window with sticky
putty once your card is in place.
5. The piece of card that you lift out
after you've cut out your shape can
be used as an additional decoration to
attach to a window or wall.
6. Backlight your silhouettes by
placing a light – such as a candle in
a jam jar or a pumpkin lantern – on
the window sill and turn out all the
other lights in the room. Remember
to make sure any candle or lantern is
secure and don't ever leave a lit one
unattended. If you're decorating the
front door, leave the hall light on.

TIPS
We used black card but you can just
as easily use orange. If the card is
not too thick and your craft knife is
sharp enough, you may want to cut
through two layers together – one
black and one orange or white – to
make the process even quicker.

USE IT OR LOSE IT
BRAIN EXERCISE
Give your grey matter a work-out

SUDOKU
The game of logic. Place each of the digits 1 to 9 in each row, column and 3x3 box. There is only one solution.

		6						
	4					7	6	
		1		5	4	2		
2			9			6		
3			4		6			1
		8			3			9
		7	5	6		3		
	8	5						9
					1			

GRAMMAR CHALLENGE
The Lynne Truss test Can you spot the errors in grammar, punctuation and spelling? See below for the correct version.

at this time of year we have to ask ourselves what we should do with all the photographs we took on holiday whether their glossy prints or stored on digital media the chances are theyll lie forgotten in a drawer well dig them out from time to time stirring vague memories of past pleasures and half forgotten people its a chore but it pays to label and date these and other family pictures so those we leave behind will not face a mountain of baffling images is that aunt doris standing by granny no silly that's not gran its gertie with aunt flo

OCTOBER'S GENERAL KNOWLEDGE QUIZ

OCTOBER'S GENERAL KNOWLEDGE QUIZ

1. Harold Wilson won his first General Election in 1964. Who did he appoint as his Chancellor of the Exchequer?
A. Roy Jenkins, B. James Callaghan, C. George Brown, D. Richard Crossman

2. Which battle was fought on St Crispin's Day, October 25, 1415?
A. Crécy, B. Agincourt, C. Poitiers D. La Rochelle

3. Which animal was said to have caused the Great Chicago Fire of 1871?
A. Mrs Murphy's horse, B. Mrs O'Gannon's sheep, C. Mrs O'Leary's cow, D. Mrs O'Doyle's goose

4. *October Road* **is an album released in 2002 by which singer-songwriter?**
A. James Taylor, B. Leonard Cohen, C. Paul Simon, D. Loudon Wainwright III

5. In which city is Martin Luther said to have nailed his 95 Theses to a church door on October 31, 1517?
A. Wittenberg, B. Cologne, C. Magdeburg, D. Worms

6. Who wrote the novel *The Hunt for Red October*?
A. Frederick Forsyth, B. Tom Clancy, C. Ken Follett, D. Alistair MacLean

7. Under which of these names did John Lennon (b. October 9, 1940) record?
A. Blind Boy Grunt, B. Dr Winston O'Boogie, C. Bijou Drains, D. Apollo C Vermouth

8. Which cartoonist (b. October, 1933) created the long-running strips *The Fosdyke Saga* **and** *Private Eye's The Cloggies*?
A. Bill Tidy, B. Larry, C. Trog, D. Ed McLaughlin

9. What was the title of Graham Greene's (b. October 2, 1904) first published novel?
A, *Stamboul Train*, B. *The Man Within*, C. *The Power and the Glory*, D. *The Name of Action*

10. What nationality was Marie Antoinette, executed October 16, 1793?
A. French, B. Spanish, C. Austrian, D. Belgian

At this time of year we have to ask ourselves what we should do with all the photographs we took on holiday – whether they're glossy prints or stored on digital media. The chances are they'll lie forgotten in a drawer: we'll dig them out from time to time, stirring vague memories of past pleasures and half-forgotten people. It's a chore, but it pays to label and date these and other family pictures, so those we leave behind will not face a mountain of baffling images. ('Is that Aunt Doris standing by Granny?' 'No, silly, that's not Gran! It's Gertie with Aunt Flo.')

6	3	2	8	4	9	1	5	7
1	8	5	3	2	7	4	9	6
4	9	7	5	6	1	3	8	2
7	2	8	9	5	4	6	3	1
3	5	9	6	7	8	2	1	4
5	1	4	2	3	6	9	7	8
9	6	3	1	8	5	7	2	4
8	4	1	7	9	2	5	6	3
2	7	6	4	1	3	8	4	5

ANSWERS
1.B, 2.B,
3.C, 4.A,
5.A, 6.B,
7.B, 8.A,
9.B, 10.C

ECUADOR

Ecuador was the first country to recognise the rights of nature in its constitution – a significant move as its rainforests are the most biodiverse regions on the planet

GETTY

FIVE Q&As

Where on earth are Ecuador's rainforests? This small South American country is divided north to south by the Andes mountain range. To the east, the River Napo snakes through the Yasuni and Cuyabeno rainforests and into bordering Peru.

How's the weather? There are two wet seasons in the Napo basin, from March to July and October to November, when monthly rainfall can reach 400mm. Visit during the drier months of August and September when the average temperature is 26C. Humidity is always high.

Will I get eaten by an alligator? Unlikely. This is the black caiman's natural habitat but catfish are plentiful so even the five-metre adults will not be hungry. The caiman all but perished until it was made illegal to sell their

skins. With just 2,000 in existence, they remain on the endangered species list. Stating the obvious, Piranha Lake is not the place to swim.

Best way to visit? From Ecuador's capital, Quito, take a short but spectacular flight over the snow-capped Andes to Coca, gateway to the Yasuni National Park. From here, board the 14-cabin Manatee Explorer, the only expedition cruiser on the Napo – so no jostling for moorings. The crew includes two conservationists. This quirky but comfortable base is ideal for discovering the Amazon basin without being tied to one place.

Any bright lights? Not surprisingly, there are no roads, cafés or shops in the rainforest. On board the Manatee, mealtimes are big social occasions. As for

shopping, you can support the indigenous tribes by buying their jewellery and crafts. Or spend an extra night in Quito and take the Pan-American Highway to Otavalo, the largest market, and shop until you drop for alpaca woollen clothes, silver jewellery and Panama hats. Don't haggle too hard – the stallholders are the friendliest you could wish to meet.

FOUR SIGHTS TO SEE

The blue morpho butterfly (below) – a devil in disguise. Jaguar, anaconda and harpy eagle are the Amazon's big three but the blue morpho wins hands down in the beauty stakes. It flirts and flutters along the river banks, and survives in great numbers because it is toxic to prey.

Parrots at the clay licks. Rainbows of cobalt-winged parakeets and

The Napo River (left); heliconia (right) growing in the rainforest

Upper Napo Valley. Young osprey swoop for fish and herons lazily flap past the exotic palm fringes in this pristine corner of the rainforest. The Manatee's crew and conservationists care deeply for the indigenous tribes and support the Cayambi people by swapping goods and bringing in supplies. In return, the tribesmen guide a chosen few to their world.

THREE THINGS TO KNOW

The Yasuni is a designated UNESCO Biosphere Reserve and home to the world's uncontactable tribes, the Tagaeri and Taromenane.

Oil accounts for more than 50% of Ecuador's exports. The Yasuni National Park is on the frontline of a global battle between nature and fossil fuels because it rests on reserves valued at $7.2 billion dollars below the Ishpingo-Tambococha-Tiputini region. This is the equivalent of 850 million barrels of crude oil. The Yasuni ITT Initiative is a proposal to leave the oil untouched, preventing the release of 400 million tonnes of CO_2 into the atmosphere, in return for half its cash value from the global community. The initiative has been heralded by the United Nations as a model in the fight to save the planet. See www.yasuni-itt.gob.ec.

The Amazon basin is home to 2,700 plant species, 100,000 different types of insects, 600 bird species, 382 species of fish, 169 species of mammals – the list goes on. Visitors are likely to encounter more wildlife in one week than in a lifetime. Toucans, macaws, weaver birds and red howler monkeys vie for attention while the three-toed sloth, tapir and woolly monkeys are the shy guys.

TWO THINGS TO AVOID

Disease. Yellow fever and malaria jabs are recommended. Avoid mosquito bites by using insect repellent with a high 'deet' content before putting on

You'll encounter more wildlife in a week than you would in a lifetime back home

lightweight, long-sleeved shirts and trousers. It's a bit of a palaver applying sun cream, then waiting 30 minutes to apply repellent, but get it down to a fine art every morning; shower, sun cream, breakfast, deet. Grab a hat and scarf and you're ready to go.

Late nights are a no-no for jungle explorers. On the equator, with sunrise at 6am and spectacular sundowns at 6pm, every minute of daylight counts. Canoes set off at dawn and after a long day's adventure, sleeping like a baby is pretty much guaranteed.

ONE MUST-DO

Take a canoe on Limoncocha Lagoon as night falls. Fireflies lace the water's edge, twinkling in time with the frogs' chorus, while fisher bats skim the surface. Do not be distracted by stars exploding into the swirling Milky Way: focus on the water. When two huge eyes break the surface, turn off your torch for some serious eye-to-eye contact with a black caiman.

Does Saga go there?
Yes, find out more about travel to Ecuador at saga.co.uk/ecuador

orange-cheeked parrots peck at the clay, which acts as an antioxidant to their diet of acidic fruits and toxic seeds.

Pink river dolphins where the Aguarico River runs into the Napo, close to the Cuyabeno Wildlife Reserve. *Boto,* as the dolphins are known by the indigenous people, blush pink when excited or anxious – just like humans. These extraordinary creatures are said to possess magical powers and are spared by the hunters.

The lake with no name. Only a few hundred people have set eyes on this tranquil oasis hidden deep in the

NOVEMBER
2014

MISTY MORNING
Near the River Ouzel,
Milton Keynes
Photograph by Saga Magazine
reader Irene Clarke

NOVEMBER

1
Saturday

2
Sunday
London to Brighton Veteran Car Rally

3
Monday

4
Tuesday

5
Wednesday
Guy Fawkes Day

6
Thursday

7
Friday

8
Saturday

9
Sunday
Remembrance Sunday

10
Monday

11
Tuesday

12
Wednesday

13
Thursday

14
Friday

15
Saturday

16
Sunday

17
Monday

18
Tuesday

Saga Magazine has everything you need to fill your days

Diary looking a bit empty this month? Pick up your copy of Saga and turn to the Out There pages.
Every month we give you details of events all over the country, from music festivals to literary
get-togethers, celebratory anniversaries and days out. We review the latest films and give you the lowdown
on what everyone's talking about – from plays, musicals and dance, to unmissable exhibitions.
And you can find even more online at **www.saga.co.uk/magazine**. To subscribe call 0800 056 1057
or go to **www.saga.co.uk/magazine-subscriptions**

19
Wednesday

20
Thursday

21
Friday

22
Saturday

23
Sunday

24
Monday

25
Tuesday

26
Wednesday

27
Thursday

28
Friday

29
Saturday

30
Sunday
St Andrew's Day

DECADE BUSTERS

NOVEMBER BIRTHDAYS

TURNING 70
Danny DeVito
(right) American actor
Sir Tim Rice *lyricist*

TURNING 60
Adam Ant *singer*

TURNING 50
Alistair McGowan
impressionist
and actor
Liza Tarbuck *TV presenter*

Roasted Chermoula Aubergines
Serves 4

Prepare 15 mins **Cook** 40 mins
2 large aubergines
2 tbsp Belazu Chermoula Paste
2 tbsp Belazu Early Harvest Extra Virgin Olive Oil
100g (4oz) Belazu Barley Couscous
125ml (4fl oz) hot vegetable stock
Zest and juice of 1 lemon
25g pack fresh mint or coriander, chopped
4 salad onions, chopped
200g (7oz) feta, crumbled
110g (4oz) Waitrose Pomegranate Seeds

1. Preheat the oven to 180C/350F/gas 4. Halve the aubergines lengthways and score deeply in a criss-cross pattern. Spread the cut sides with Belazu Chermoula Paste and place on a baking sheet. Drizzle with a little of the Belazu Early Harvest Extra Virgin Olive Oil and bake for 30-40 minutes until dark and tender.
2. Meanwhile, place the Belazu Barley Couscous in a large bowl and pour over the hot stock, lemon zest and juice. Set aside until the stock has been absorbed, then stir in the mint, salad onions, feta, pomegranate and remaining oil.
3. Scoop the centre out of each aubergine half, leaving the skin intact. Roughly mash the removed flesh and stir into the couscous, then spoon the mixture back into the aubergine shells. Serve just warm.
Recipe and photograph from Waitrose. More than 5,000 recipes can be found at www.waitrose.com/recipes

THIS WEEK'S TOP TIP
Protect exotic plants over winter

GARDENING
Non-native plants can survive a tough British winter with a bit of help. Tie up palms and spiky plants such as phormiums and cordylines, bringing their leaves together and wrapping them round with garden string, to protect the vulnerable growing point at the top of the stem. Add a layer of horticultural fleece to be on the safe side, or pack straw round the leaves, holding it in place by winding round a layer of fleece.

Shift succulents to a greenhouse, potting shed (if it has a window) or even to a porch – anywhere that will keep the rain off.

Trim back the foliage on pots of cannas and dahlias and other tender bulbs, leaving about 5cm (2in) of growth, then bring them under cover into a shed, garage or greenhouse.

Protect outdoor pots too. Wrap ceramic or terracotta pots with bubble wrap to prevent frost damage to pots and plants within. And stand pots on special pot feet (or use old bricks) so that water can drain away and reduce the chance of the plant roots rotting or freezing.

ALL THINGS BRIGHT AND BEAUTIFUL
Hedgehogs
Depending on the weather, hedgehogs may have already gone into hibernation, but if you see a small one snuffling around, it's likely to be one of this year's second litter trying to build up its body mass before the big sleep. Put down some cat food to help – but not bread and milk. Remember, if you've set up a bonfire, shift and re-stack it before lighting – you never know what's underneath.

Handbags and gladrags

Cast-off clothes are no longer 'old' - they're vintage.
And most desirable of all are designer handbags:
the prices below will send you rushing to the attic

Some women's clothes and accessories from the past few decades have been cleverly rebranded 'vintage'. Throwaways that used to crop up at charity jumble sales are attracting increasingly high asking prices. While this trend continues, cast-offs from the 1950s, 60s, 70s and 80s might be worth rescuing from wherever you may have discarded them.

An anonymous old leather handbag is the sort of object you now see marked up to £50 or more. Designer handbags in ostrich, crocodile, snakeskin or lizard are less likely to be lurking in forgotten corners. If you do happen to find one with a label saying Louis Vuitton, Gucci or Hermès, crack open the vintage champagne.

Of all the top makes, Hermès seems to have the most allure. In her prime, you might have thought the singer and film star Jane Birkin had all she wanted, but when she met the chairman of Hermès she complained about how difficult it was to find a serviceable weekend handbag. That momentous meeting led to the birth of the Birkin bag. One 'vintage' example recently sold for £37,250. Now that would be attic heaven.

SOLD
Like Jane Birkin, Grace Kelly also gave her name to a Hermès bag. A black, crocodile number fetched £17,196 at Bonhams in Los Angeles in June 2012, after a similar one was withdrawn from sale in 2010

REDISCOVERED BOOK

'The funniest account of an Edwardian upbringing'

Look Back with Love
Dodie Smith
(Slightly Foxed Edition, £16)

Dodie Smith's biographer has described this as 'one of the happiest and funniest accounts of an Edwardian upbringing'. And indeed it is. Best known for *I Capture the Castle* and the evergreen *The Hundred and One Dalmatians*, Dodie did not publish this account until she was 78. Her memoir gives a wonderful picture of a large extended family and of the funny, complicated, creative little girl who would later say, 'I think I'm an oddity really, but I do my very, very best to write well.'

As chosen by the staff of Slightly Foxed bookshop, specialists in unusual titles, old and new; www.foxedbooks.com

'God, I get so fed up with these cartoonists having a pop at middle-aged people, making out that all we do is moan about things.'

THIS WEEK'S TOP TIP
Dealing with cold feet

HEALTH

A hot-water bottle is the instant solution when your feet are freezing cold, but it can have unwanted repercussions. The heat can make the blood flow too quickly into the feet for the blood vessels to cope with (especially as the blood vessels will have contracted due to the cold), which is one of the causes of chilblains. (You can also get chilblains on your hands and even the tip of your nose or your ears, for exactly the same reason.) It's much better to deal with the problem gradually by massaging your feet – or getting someone else to do this for you – and then putting on thick socks and a pair of slippers and letting them warm up gradually.

RECIPE OF THE WEEK
Winter Soup with Bacon, Lentil & Pasta
Serves 4

Prepare 10 mins **Cook** 30 mins

200g (7oz) Waitrose Free Range Smoked
*   Dry Cured Lardons*
1 onion, chopped
2 garlic cloves, chopped
1 celery stalk, chopped
1 carrot, diced
2 tomatoes, chopped
200g (7oz) Waitrose Love Life Green Lentils
1.5 litres (2½ pints) hot chicken stock
100g (4oz) Waitrose Orzo
25g pack flat-leaf parsley, chopped

1. Cook the lardons, chopped onion, garlic, celery and diced carrot in a large saucepan for 5 minutes until the bacon lardons begin to crisp – there should be enough oil in the lardons so you won't need to add more.
2. Add the chopped tomatoes, cook for 1-2 minutes or until pulpy, then stir in the lentils and stock. Bring to the boil, cover and simmer for 15 minutes.
3. Add the orzo pasta and cook for a further 8-10 minutes until both the lentils and pasta are tender. Stir in the parsley, then ladle into bowls and serve with plenty of black pepper.
Recipe and photograph from Waitrose. More than 5,000 recipes can be found at www.waitrose.com/recipes

DON'T QUOTE ME, BUT...
'The only time I ever enjoyed ironing was the day I accidentally got gin in the steam iron'
Phyllis Diller

ALL THINGS BRIGHT AND BEAUTIFUL
Making sloe gin
Picking sloes after the first frost is said to improve their flavour, but if there's a bumper harvest, why wait? Put them in the freezer overnight instead; this also means you won't have to prick each sloe with a needle to allow the juice to blend with the gin, as freezing splits their skins. Tip them into sterilised wide-necked bottles or jars, add slightly less sugar than fruit (by weight), top up with (cheap) gin and wait a couple of months, shaking weekly.

**NOVEMBER
DRINK OF THE MONTH**

MONK'S SPICED MULLED WINE

Just the thing to serve at
a fireworks party

1 orange
12 cloves
3 tbsp soft brown sugar
1 whole nutmeg, grated
3 cinnamon sticks
2 lemons, sliced
1 bottle dry red wine

Stud the orange with the
cloves and place it in a large
saucepan. Add the sugar,
grated nutmeg, cinnamon sticks,
lemon slices and 500ml (17fl oz)
water. Then stir over a low
heat until the sugar has dissolved.
Bring to the boil, reduce the
heat and simmer for 15 minutes.
Finally, add the red wine and
heat through. Serves 4-6.

'THEY ADOPT A CODE THAT THEY THINK I CAN'T UNDERSTAND'

But they've got it all wrong – Badger always
knows what the DFLs are talking about

I'm not allowed on the sofa.
Apparently. We have three sofas
in the house. One in the TV room,
and two in the lounge. I'm not
allowed on any of them. In theory. But
then I'm not allowed on BOG's
favourite reading chair, or the top
step of the stairs, or the rattan chair in
the hall... or many other places.

Once I overheard the DFLs saying
that it was 'best to let sleeping dogs
lie' because then I wouldn't pester
them for a walk. But they don't use
the 'W' word in front of me. Instead
they adopt a code that is supposed to
be impossible for me to understand.
So a walk is a 'wubblewoo' or 'wub'
for short; a bone is a 'bobo'; a biscuit
is a 'biccy', and so on. They haven't
got one for a visit to the vet, but
I have. I call it 'hell'.

The first couple of times I went
to the vet's they insisted on sticking
a thermometer somewhere eye-
bulgingly uncomfortable.
'OWWWWWW, NO YOU IDIOTS!'
I yelped. 'I'VE GOT A MICROCHIP IN
MY NECK! ANYBODY KNOWS YOU
CAN MEASURE BODY TEMPERATURE
FROM THAT!!' Finally a nice young
vet called Megan, who isn't much
older than me, pointed this out and it
hasn't happened since.

Whenever we get home after the
vet's I'll get something like: 'Does she
want some biccies, because she's
such a brave girl?' Of course I want
some biccies. I'm hungry. I'm a dog.
All I think about is food. And rabbits.
And cats (GRRRR. I think a lot about
them). And, of course, my boyfriend
Wilf (I think about him a lot, too). And
walks. Of course I want to go for a walk.
It's what I do. 'Does she want to go
for a wubblewoo?' YES! What d'you
think? I'M A DOG, for Dog's sake!

There is, of course, one time when
I don't want to go for a walk, and
that's when the village holds its
fireworks party. Why they derive such
pleasure from making loud bangs
is a mystery. There's only one place
for a dog with sensitive hearing in
such circumstances, and that's under
the bed with a sock in each ear.

Nickname this month: *Poodly
Woodly Winky Woo. GRRR.*
Best moment: *Stole the remote
control again and hid it in the bushes.*

**Let sleeping
dogs lie, as they
say at home**

RECIPE OF THE WEEK
Spiced Beef with Garlic & Oyster Sauce
Serves 2

Prepare 15 mins **Cook** 10 mins

1½ tbsp Lee Kum Kee Premium Oyster Flavoured Sauce
1½ tbsp Lee Kum Kee Black Bean Garlic Sauce
2 tsp sugar
1 lime, halved
250g (9oz) rump steak, trimmed of fat and
*   thinly sliced into strips*
1 tbsp groundnut oil
Pinch chilli flakes
300g pack Waitrose Vibrant & Fresh Super
*   Bright Pan Fry Vegetables*
150g (5oz) basmati rice, cooked

1. Mix together the oyster and black bean garlic sauces in a bowl with the sugar and juice of ½ lime. Add the beef strips and stir to coat. Set aside for 10 minutes.
2. Heat the oil in a wok or large frying pan over a high heat. When smoking, remove the beef with a slotted spoon, reserving the sauce, and add to the wok with the chilli flakes. Stir-fry for 2 minutes to brown, then transfer to a plate.
3. Add the pan fry vegetables to the hot wok and stir-fry for 2 minutes. Return the beef and the reserved sauce to the wok and continue to cook for a further 2–3 minutes until sticky and piping hot.
4. Divide the cooked rice between 2 warmed bowls and top with the sticky beef and vegetables. Serve with the remaining lime half cut into wedges for squeezing.
Recipe and photograph from Waitrose. More than 5,000 recipes can be found at www.waitrose.com/recipes

THIS WEEK'S TOP TIP
Make a will

MONEY
If you die without making a will, the government will decide who gets what from your estate – far better to make that decision yourself. If you plan to DIY, rather than going to a solicitor (you can buy a kit from a stationer's or download forms online), it is crucial to sign your will and have it formally witnessed. Witnesses must be over 18 and can't be beneficiaries in the will. Make sure that family members know where your will is kept – either in a safe place at home, with your bank or your solicitor. November is usually Will Aid month, when solicitors will prepare your will free in exchange for a donation to the charity Will Aid.

ALL THINGS BRIGHT AND BEAUTIFUL
Starling roost
Just before dusk, hundreds of thousands of starlings gather in the sky, performing spectacular feats before settling down for the night. The advantages of gathering in such vast numbers include protection from predators and keeping warm. Famous starling roosts include Brighton Pier and Leicester Square in London. But don't be fooled by the sight of so many birds – the population has crashed in recent years and it is now an endangered species.

DON'T QUOTE ME, BUT...
'A government that robs Peter to pay Paul can always depend on the support of Paul'
George Bernard Shaw

TINY ISLANDS
MURDER AND MYSTERY

Agatha Christie used this island as the setting
for her bestselling novel of all time

BURGH ISLAND
Opposite Bigbury-on-Sea,
Devon
Size: 26 acres
Population: c. 30

Unlike most tidal islands, there's rather less of an imperative to keep an eye on the waves, for down below sits Burgh Island's most photographed attraction – the sea tractor.

Built in 1969 to carry visitors back and forth safely above the brine, whether foaming or not, this unique beast runs on demand from about eight in the morning to as late as midnight, if needs be. The monstrous roar of the engine and the Tonka Toy look of its Brobdingnagian wheels have men and boys dancing from foot to foot with glee. It is an extraordinary thing to ride upon and, at £2 each way, is an admirable way of partaking in the life of Burgh Island without breaking the bank.

Well known though Burgh Island is, there can be no doubt that it is far more famous as a fictional entity than it is when merely playing itself. For the reasons why, look no further than a crime solved by a Belgian detective and a murder mystery in which absolutely everyone dies, for this island is the setting of not just one but two Agatha Christie novels – *Evil Under the Sun* and, her biggest seller of all, *And Then There Were None*.

Christie was one of many celebrities who visited Burgh Island's hotel in the 1930s. Fans of the hotel in those troubled times were an eclectic bunch that included Noël Coward, songstress Josephine Baker, speedster Malcolm Campbell and George Formby, among many others.

To discover the particular attraction that this little green hump off the south Devon coast had for the rich and famous, we have to go back to a music-hall entertainer named George Chirgwin, aka 'The White-Eyed Kaffir' (not a name, one suspects, he would have used today). He made

a mint singing falsetto and bought Burgh Island in 1895 for £100, erecting the island's first ever hotel, a small wooden affair.

However, it was left to a later owner, Archie Nettlefold, to build the establishment that drew the stars down to Devon. He commissioned an architect to build him a concrete house with the air of a castle about it. The result was an elegant, bright white Art Deco pile that was completed in 1929. After a chequered history, the current owners took over in 2001 and made the hotel even more luxurious.

The island is eminently roamable, with only the eastern part (the grounds of the hotel) off limits. Reached by crossing a beach from the small resort of Bigbury-on-Sea, its grassy slopes rise abruptly about 200ft to the summit of its one hill, with cliffs around the western shores and, to the south, a tiny headland.

HOW TO GET THERE
From Plymouth station, walk down to the Barbican (0.75 miles) where you can pick up the no 93 bus to Modbury. Then it's a breezy 5.5-mile hike or taxi ride to Bigbury-on-Sea, from where you can stroll across to Burgh Island at low tide. When the tide is in, you can pick up the famous Burgh Island sea tractor (8am until late evening).

EXTRACTED FROM *Tiny Islands* BY DIXE WILLS (AA PUBLISHING, £14.99)

RECIPE OF THE WEEK
Iced Rosette Ginger Cake
Serves 8-10

Prepare 15 mins **Cook** 35-40 mins

125g (4½oz) butter
125g (4½oz) dark brown
    muscovado sugar
200g (7oz) golden syrup,
    plus 2 tbsp
3 pieces Waitrose Chinese
    Stem Ginger, finely
    chopped, plus 2 tbsp
    syrup from the jar
250g (9oz) Homepride
    Self-Raising Flour
3 tsp ground ginger

1 tsp bicarbonate of soda
50g (2oz) essential
    Waitrose Sultanas
2 large eggs, beaten
250ml (9fl oz) milk
500g (1lb) Waitrose
    Christmas Ready to Roll
    White Icing
Icing sugar, for dusting

1. Preheat the oven to 180C/350F/gas 4. Grease and line the base of a 20cm (8in) round cake tin with non-stick baking parchment.
2. Place the butter, sugar, 200g (7oz) golden syrup and the chopped ginger and syrup together in a small saucepan and heat gently, stirring until the butter has melted.
3. Place the flour, ground ginger, bicarbonate of soda and sultanas in a large bowl.
4. In a jug, whisk together the eggs and milk. Pour the melted syrup mixture and the egg mixture into the bowl of flour and beat well with a wooden spoon until blended. Pour the mixture into the prepared tin and bake for 35-40 minutes, or until a skewer comes out clean.
5. Leave the cake to cool in its tin, then invert the cooled cake onto a serving plate so that the flat bottom is uppermost. Brush with the remaining golden syrup.
6. Roll out the icing on a sugar-dusted surface to the thickness of a pound coin. Using a 3cm (1in) cutter, stamp out as many discs as possible. Arrange them in overlapping rings. Leave to set for a couple of hours before slicing.
Recipe and photograph from Waitrose. More than 5,000 recipes can be found at www.waitrose.com/recipes

THIS WEEK'S TOP TIP
Making eyes

BEAUTY
For a natural, lasting look, start by applying a base colour to your eyelids that matches your skin tone.
    Build up colour by sweeping a medium-toned eyeshadow over the lid and about three-quarters of the way up the eye, taking it close to the lashes too. To emphasise your lids, add a wide band of shadow in a deep neutral shade – it will help them stand out more when your eyes are open. To enhance the curved shape of the lids, add a darker tone mid-lid, and feather it outwards towards the eyebrow.

DON'T QUOTE ME, BUT...

'Count your age by friends, not years. Count your life by smiles, not tears'

John Lennon

ALL THINGS BRIGHT AND BEAUTIFUL
Fieldfares
If you've seen a flock of 'thrushes' in winter, chances are they were fieldfares, regular visitors from Scandinavia. They begin by feeding on berries, moving on to grubs and worms once supplies dry up. Generally they avoid gardens but in severe weather are forced into closer contact with humans. If you spot them in yours, try putting out a wrinkly apple or pear that's on the turn – and watch how competitive the birds are.

MAJOR DESIGN FAULT

November 2014 is the 97th anniversary of:
an underwater pile-up caused by water down the chimney in a K-class sub

ROYAL NAVAL MUSEUM

K-class submarines weren't a great success; of the 18 built, six sank in accidents and only one ever engaged an enemy vessel, ramming a U-boat after its torpedo failed to explode. So they would be able to keep up with surface vessels, they had steam engines – and consequently needed funnels – but this led to a problem when manoeuvring: seawater coming down the chimney and putting the boiler out.

When this happened to K4 in November 1917, she lost power and K1 collided with her. Fatally holed, K1 was abandoned and then scuttled by gunfire from the cruiser HMS Blonde, the ship the subs were accompanying to prevent enemy capture.

WOTEVA!
Teenage translator

Nerdjacking
To nerdjack the conversation is to suddenly go into lots of unnecessary technical detail, inappropriate for the knowledge and interest of the listener

Swagger
To move with grace and confidence and to dress with style. Shall we let them think they made that one up? Should we?

Untag
To dissociate oneself from a group of people one considers to be socially embarrassing

— CLIVE COLLINS —

'You came in drunk last night – I heard you fumbling with the cat flap.'

DID YOU KNOW?
Stat attack

You have more chance of guessing someone's phone number correctly than winning the Lottery

The British office worker drinks an average four cups of tea and one cup of coffee each day

Portugal is England's oldest ally. The Anglo-Portuguese Treaty signed in 1373 is still in force

Let me out!

Name: Terry
Owner's name: Sam Amos
Best habit: Going to sleep in a slipper
Worst habit: Diving headfirst off the kitchen step
Likes: Dandelions, bananas, strawberries
Dislikes: Getting stuck on his back
Personality:
Escaping is always on his mind
Naughtiest moment:
Biting people's toes
Most human trait: Loves sunbathing

TOP TECHIE TIP
Pinterest rates

Social networks are evolving as new sites are developed to fill specific niches. And perhaps none has made a bigger impact than Pinterest: a virtual 'pinboard' for sharing pictures and videos. Its growing appeal lies in the way it showcases these. Register at pinterest.com and when that's all done, you can start searching for categories that interest you. For example, search for 'Food and Drink' and you will be met with an array of photos, each representing the cover of a pinboard. Apps for iPhone, Android and iPad enable you to 'pin' while out and about.

JOKE OF THE MONTH
Did you hear about the cannibals that attended a wedding? **They toasted the bride and groom.**

sent in by Elizabeth Williams

HOW TO MAKE FINGERLESS GLOVES

These stripy gloves are warm and stylish but leave your fingers free. You can make them shorter by reducing the number of rows between rows 33 and 47, or longer by knitting extra rows before decreasing

YOU WILL NEED
- *25g (1oz) of 4-ply wool in colour A (col A) – brown*
- *25g (1oz) of 4-ply wool in colour B (col B) – aubergine*
- *25g (1oz) of 4-ply wool in colour C (col C) – moss*
- *3.25mm (UK size 10; US size 3) knitting needles*

ABBREVIATIONS
cont continue
*col colour, **dec** decrease/decreasing*
inc increase/increasing
*k knit, **p** purl,*
*rep repeat, * repeat from*
*RS right side, **st/sts** stitches*
tog together

TENSION
14sts and 18 rows = 5cm (2in). Finished length is 26cm (10¼in).

TO MAKE THE RIGHT GLOVE
With 3.25mm (UK size 10; US size 3) needles and col B, cast on 59sts. Change to col A and work 6 rows in k1, p1 rib. Dec 1st at end of row 6. (58sts) (For decreasing, knit together the 3rd and 4th sts from the edge. This produces a fashioning mark on the gloves, which gives them a more stylish finish.)

Cont with col A. **Row 1 (RS):** Knit. **Row 2:** Purl. **Row 3:** Using col B, knit. **Row 4:** Purl. **Row 5:** Using col C, knit. **Row 6:** Purl. These 6 rows form the pattern.

Cont in pattern for stripes, dec 1st at each end of the following row and then on rows 15, 21, 27 and 33, until 48sts remain.

Cont until the beginning of row 47, then work thumb gusset as follows, keeping stripes correct. **Row 1 (RS):** K24, inc in next st, k2, inc in next st, k20. (50sts)

Work 3 rows. **Row 5:** K24, inc in next st, k4, inc in next st, k20. (52sts)

Work 3 rows. **Row 9:** K24, inc in next st, k6, inc in next st, k20. (54sts) Work 3 rows. **Row 13:** K24, inc in next st, k8, inc in next st, k20. (56sts) Work 3 rows. **Row 17:** K24, inc in next st, k10, inc in next st, k20. (58sts) Work 1 row. **Row 19:** K38, turn and cast on 1st.

Row 20*: p14, turn and cast on 1st. (15sts) Work 6 rows on these 15sts, keeping stripes correct.

Change to col A and work 2 rows in k1, p1 rib. Cast off with col B. Join the thumb seam. With right sides facing, rejoin yarn, pick up 4sts from the thumb base (2 either side of seam) and cont to end of row.

Work 16 rows more. Change to col A and work 4 rows in k1, p1 rib. Change to col B and cast off.

TO MAKE THE LEFT GLOVE
Work as right glove to the beginning of thumb gusset shaping. Then work as follows: **Row 1 (RS):** K19, inc in next st, k2, inc in next st, k25. (50sts)

Work 3 rows. **Row 5:** K19, inc in next st, k4, inc in next st, k25. (52sts) Work 3 rows. **Row 9:** K19, inc in next st, k6, inc in next st, k25. (54sts) Work 3 rows. **Row 13:** K19, inc in next st, k8, inc in next st, k25. (56sts) Work 3 rows. **Row 17:** K19, inc in next st, k10, inc in next st, k25. (58sts) Work 1 row. **Row 19:** K33, turn and cast on 1st, cont as for right glove from *.

MAKING UP
Sew the side seam with mattress stitch, catching in ends where you can. Then sew in any remaining ends and press lightly with the iron on the wool setting.

USE IT OR LOSE IT
BRAIN EXERCISE
Give your grey matter a work-out

SUDOKU
The game of logic. Place each of the digits 1 to 9 in each row, column and 3x3 box. There is only one solution.

	2						7	6
4	8			5				
			9	3				
9		6					3	
	6		3		7		8	
	3			1				2
		5	1					
		8				7	6	
4	7					1		

GRAMMAR CHALLENGE
The Lynne Truss test Can you spot the errors in grammar, punctuation and spelling? See below for the correct version.

uh oh the glooms arriving every morning we wake up and the world is a little darker we look back with fondness to passed summers but right now even a damp day in may is rather more appealing than the rather bedraggled hangdog look on the face of many of our gardens at this time of year it need not be this way there are loads of plants waiting around for precisely this moment the time they can glow radiantly against the grey clouds and shine out against the teatime murkiness the most obvious of course is the evergreen

NOVEMBER'S GENERAL KNOWLEDGE QUIZ

1. Who designed Princess Elizabeth's wedding dress in 1947?
A. Hardy Amies, B. Norman Hartnell, C. Coco Chanel, D. Dior

2. Which New York store sponsors the city's annual Thanksgiving Parade?
A. Sears, B. Macy's, C. Bloomingdales, D. Tiffany

3. Cricketing legend Sir Ian Botham (b. November 24, 1955) played in the Football League, but for which club?
A. Scunthorpe Utd, B. Doncaster Rovers C. Bristol City, D. Chesterfield

4. Which national holiday on November 11 (our Remembrance Day) honours US servicemen and women?
A. Armed Forces Day, B. Patriots Day, C. Veterans Day, D. Campaign Day

5. From which grape is Beaujolais nouveau made?
A. Gamay, B. Gouget noir, C. Malbec, D. Merille

6. Linda Evans (b. November 19, 1942) played which character in *Dynasty*?
A. Fallon, B. Sable, C. Krystle, D. Amanda

7. In what year was Microsoft Windows 1.0 released?
A. 1984, B. 1985, C. 1986, D. 1987

8. Which Russian author was sentenced to death (later commuted) in 1849 for anti-government activities?
A. Dostoevsky, B. Tolstoy, C. Turgenev, D. Gogol

9. From which building did the Warren Commission claim the shots were fired that killed President John Kennedy in 1963?
A. Texas Book Depository,
B. Dallas Grain Futures Building,
C. The Lone Star Assurance and Loans Company,
D. Dallas City Attorney's Office

10. Jamie Lee Curtis made her name in the horror film *Halloween*. Which Hollywood star was her mother?
A. Debbie Reynolds, B. Janet Leigh, C. Tippi Hedren, D. Ava Gardner

Uh-oh. The gloom's arriving. Every morning we wake up and the world is a little darker. We look back with fondness to past summers; but right now, even a damp day in May is rather more appealing than the rather bedraggled, hangdog look on the face of many of our gardens at this time of year. It need not be this way. There are loads of plants waiting around for precisely this moment: the time they can glow radiantly against the grey clouds and shine out against the teatime murkiness. The most obvious, of course, is the evergreen.

4	7	3	9	5	6	1	2	8
1	2	9	8	3	4	7	6	5
6	8	5	1	7	2	6	4	3
8	3	7	5	4	1	9	6	2
2	9	6	3	8	7	5	1	4
5	6	1	2	9	8	2	4	7
9	1	2	5	6	7	8	4	3
3	4	8	7	6	5	2	1	9
6	7	8	3	1	4	2	9	5

ANSWERS
1. B, 2. B,
3. A, 4. C,
5. A, 6. C,
7. B, 8. A,
9. A, 10. B

KERALA

Kerala is a lush and fertile land where pineapples, banana trees and coconut palms flourish – where the local people say if you stand still for more than a minute, you will grow a few inches

FIVE Q&As

Where on earth is it? Kerala is in southwest India, tucked in between the Lakshadweep Sea and the Western Ghats. To the north is Karnataka with Tamil Nadu to the east.

How's the weather? It rains for one third of the year, creating a vivid green landscape. The monsoon rains start in June and do not subside until December. Make the most of this tropical climate with a late winter or early spring visit, when temperatures average 28-32C.

Will I see beggars or snake charmers? Unlikely. Kerala does not suffer the level of poverty that is associated with big cities. In fact, this small state offers the highest quality of life in India. Its people live well off the land and average life expectancy is 74 years. The literacy rate is now 94% and rising.

Any bright lights? Life is a celebration in Kerala. From snakeboat races to the Onam harvest festival,

religious festivals and elephant processions, it seems there is always dancing in the street. Even the smallest village bursts into colour with decorations, music and street processions. Children light candles outside temples and their smiles will light up your life.

Best way to visit? Fly to Cochin. From here, start a tour of the three main geographical regions; the mountains, lakes and coastline. It's essential to explore them all to discover the soul of Kerala.

FOUR SIGHTS TO SEE

Lakes at Alappuzha. Stay on a houseboat on Lake Vembanad, using it as a base to meander along the labyrinth of canals in Thekkady. In the evening stroll to Puthangadi, where villagers knock cashew nuts from trees and sell them on the roadside, along with sardines. As evening comes and the temperature cools, every generation steps outside to shop in the market or chat to neighbours while the children swim and play cricket. Join in: life here's like stepping back 50 years.

The Western Ghats, mountains that rise and fall 2,600m, including vast tea plantations. Gardeners will take inspiration from the shape and form of dramatic, green hillside planting.

Unwind on the Malabar coast with its white sandy beaches. At Marari Beach Resort stay in thatched villas overlooking the sea and in the morning watch the fishermen bring in their haul. When you're lazing in your hammock between the coconut palms, hoist a yellow flag to alert the waiter. He will bring you another, drink, snack, towel... You'll be

Taking it easy, Kerala-style
Messing about in a houseboat along the backwaters *(main picture)*; the *pongala* ceremony *(right)* is for women only, who make offerings to the goddess Devi; elephant processions are an everyday occurrence *(below)*

following the example of Paul McCartney and Heather Mills, who honeymooned here.

Spice up your life at a plantation. Kerala produces an abundance of high-quality spices including pepper, ginger, cardamom, nutmeg, cloves and vanilla, which make hugely acceptable presents to take home. Pick pepper from a tree and learn how tamarind flavours so much of the local cuisine. When you're back in the

A synchronised head-to-toe massage will leave you feeling on top of the world

in 1498 and opened the way for European colonisation – with Portuguese, Dutch and British fighting for control of the lucrative spice trade.

TWO THINGS TO REMEMBER

Drink only bottled water. Check the lid is sealed before you buy and do not take chances.

Join a dawn yoga class. Whether it is on a beach or at a retreat, Kerala offers a unique tantric form of yoga which combines hatha yoga with an ancient martial art called *kalaripayattu*.

ONE MUST-DO

Have an Ayurvedic treatment. Over the centuries Ayurvedic practitioners have developed medicinal preparations and therapies to promote wellbeing. These plant-based treatments are prescribed to maintain the health of mind, body and spirit. Even if you are fighting fit, visit an Ayurvedic centre. When the two masseurs pour warm oil over your body to start a synchronised head-to-toe massage you will feel on top of the world. Popular treatments include: *dhara*, herbal oils and medicated buttermilk poured on the forehead and body to help with insomnia and tension; *njavarakizhi*, to ease arthritic conditions and skin problems; *udvarthanam*, a massage with herbal powders to fight obesity and rheumatic disorders.

UK, serve an apple pie and boast how you scraped the cinnamon bark yourself from a tree.

THREE THINGS TO KNOW

Kerala has the first freely elected communist government in the world. It came to power in 1957 and has held power ever since from Kerala's difficult-to-pronounce capital, Thiruvananthapuram.

Kerala boasts India's biggest fishing industry. Seafood is served with almost every meal and is perfect for the Western palate, served fresh and full of flavour, but not too spicy. Try the speciality kingfish curry followed by *parippu payasam*, a dessert made from rice cooked in thick coconut milk and a jaggery (sugar) syrup. Agriculture is also important to the region: bananas, pineapples and coconuts all flourish in the fertile soil.

Portuguese explorer Vasco da Gama was buried in St Francis Church, Cochin. Built in 1503, it is the oldest European church in India. Centuries later da Gama's body was returned to Lisbon, but the church is significant as a silent witness to the European colonial struggle with the subcontinent.

The Cheras ruled much of Kerala in the Middle Ages until da Gama arrived

Does Saga go there?
Yes, find out more about travel to Kerala at saga.co.uk/india

DECEMBER
2014

FROZEN LANDSCAPE

Rural West Midlands

Photograph by Saga Magazine
reader Ray Barley

DECEMBER

1
Monday

2
Tuesday

3
Wednesday

4
Thursday

5
Friday

6
Saturday

7
Sunday

8
Monday

9
Tuesday

10
Wednesday

11
Thursday

12
Friday

13
Saturday

14
Sunday

15
Monday

16
Tuesday

17
Wednesday

18
Thursday

Saga Magazine has everything you need to fill your days

Diary looking a bit empty this month? Pick up your copy of Saga and turn to the Out There pages.
Every month we give you details of events all over the country, from music festivals to literary
get-togethers, celebratory anniversaries and days out. We review the latest films and give you the lowdown
on what everyone's talking about – from plays, musicals and dance, to unmissable exhibitions.
And you can find even more online at **www.saga.co.uk/magazine**. To subscribe call 0800 056 1057
or go to **www.saga.co.uk/magazine-subscriptions**

19
Friday

20
Saturday

21
Sunday

22
Monday

23
Tuesday

24
Wednesday

25
Thursday
Christmas Day

26
Friday
Boxing Day

27
Saturday

28
Sunday

29
Monday

30
Tuesday

31
Wednesday

DECADE BUSTERS

DECEMBER BIRTHDAYS

TURNING 70
Neil Innes *musician*
Jane Lapotaire *actress*

TURNING 60
Denzel Washington *American actor*
Annie Lennox *(right) singer*
Alex Salmond *Scotland's First Minister*

TURNING 50
Robson Green
actor

RECIPE OF THE WEEK
Chocolate Orange Profiteroles
Serves 6

Prepare 20 mins **Cook** 30 mins
75g (3oz) essential Waitrose Dairy Butter
2 tbsp caster sugar
60g (2½oz) plain flour
*2 medium Waitrose Columbian Blacktail Free Range Eggs,
  beaten*
*100g Waitrose Continental Plain Chocolate, broken into
  small pieces*
Finely grated zest and juice of 1 orange
300ml (½ pint) essential Waitrose Whipping Cream

1. Put 50g (2oz) of the butter, 1 tbsp of the sugar and 150ml
(5fl oz) water into a pan, stir until the butter has melted,
then bring to the boil. Add the flour all in one go then, using
a wooden spoon, beat vigorously, cooking for 1-2 minutes
until the mixture leaves the sides of the pan and forms
a ball. Turn off the heat and leave to cool for 5 minutes.
2. Heat the oven to 180C/350F/gas 4. Gradually beat the
eggs into the dough, a little at a time, to make a thick batter.
Drop 18 small tsps of the mixture, spaced well apart, on
2 baking sheets that are lined with baking parchment. Bake
for 20 minutes until puffed and dark golden — don't be
tempted to take them out of the oven early as they may
look done but need to cook all the way through. Transfer to
a wire rack and leave to cool completely.
3. Place the chocolate, remaining 25g (1oz) butter and the
orange juice in a heatproof bowl and sit over a pan of
simmering water. Heat gently for 5 minutes or so, stirring
from time to time, until the chocolate melts. Stir in the
grated zest.
4. Whisk the cream and remaining 1 tbsp sugar together
until firm. Make a hole in the side of each profiterole and
gently fill with cream using either a piping bag or small
teaspoon. Divide the profiteroles between serving bowls and
drizzle with the chocolate orange sauce. Serve straightaway.
*Recipe and photograph from Waitrose. More than 5,000
recipes can be found at www.waitrose.com/recipes*

THIS WEEK'S TOP TIP
Planning ahead

GARDENING
Time to indulge in a spot
of armchair gardening –
a favourite time of year for
many plot-holders.
Whether you prefer to leaf
through a catalogue or
browse online, seed and
plant suppliers are keen to
tempt you with the latest
must-haves, from strangely
coloured petunias to
unusual vegetables.

It's all too easy to
over-order, especially if
you have only a small
garden. Bear in mind that
seed packets often contain
masses of seeds, so it can
be worth getting together
with fellow gardeners,
making a list and trying to
agree on a shared order.

While you're putting pen
to paper, it's a good time
to make a plan of your
garden – a scale one, if you
brave the elements and
take some measurements
– and write down all your
grand plans for your
plot, and the best time of
year to execute them.

ALL THINGS BRIGHT AND BEAUTIFUL
Robins
Robins are fiercely territorial, staking out their patch and
declaring it loudly in song. But they have no hesitation in
taking things further and fighting off intruders (ground-
breaking experiments done in the 1930s record a
robin attacking a stuffed bird encroaching on its territory).
The tradition of robins on Christmas cards dates back
to Victorian times, when postmen wore red jackets and
were nicknamed 'robins'. Envelopes often depicted
a robin delivering a letter or card and eventually the birds
became associated with Christmas cards.

DON'T QUOTE ME, BUT...
'In Hollywood a marriage
is a success if it outlasts milk'
Rita Rudner

REDISCOVERED BOOK

'Plans for a quiet village Christmas are dashed'

High Rising
Angela Thirkell
(Virago, £8.99)

When Laura goes to spend Christmas at her cottage in the village of High Rising, she is expecting a quiet time. Miss Grey, a new arrival in the village, is secretary to the extremely rich George Knox and is intent on improving her position by marrying her wealthy boss. Laura has to rescue her neighbour from his employee's clutches and, at the same time, help his daughter secure the hand of the man she loves – so not a quiet time at all.

As chosen by the staff of Slightly Foxed bookshop, specialists in unusual titles, old and new; www.foxedbooks.com

Record-breaking prices

It's time to dust off your vinyl albums and singles – who knows, you might have a rarity among them. If not, just enjoy listening to them again

Many of us regret disposing of our record collections in a house move or general clear-out. Vinyl is making a comeback, so let's hope you were lucky or lazy enough to hang on to yours. Perhaps your record player has never stopped turning, but if your collection is languishing in the attic, now is the time to take another look. Most of your albums will probably be worth a tenner or so, provided the cover is presentable and the

record unscratched. You may come across a hidden gem – but probably not a signed 1967 Parlophone issue of The Beatles' *Sgt Pepper's Lonely Hearts Club Band*, which sold last year for £190,000, shooting it to the top of the most expensive records chart.

Relatively obscure records can also be highly collectable. A rare 1967 promo single of a little-known American singer called Junior McCants sold for £9,358 on eBay with bidding starting at £6. He died before his career had a chance to flourish – but not before he'd made an impact on mods in Manchester during the era of Northern Soul.

SOLD

A Pete Townshend guitar might also appeal. This one featured in The Who's comeback performance at Live Aid in 1985 and sold at Christie's for £34,850 in November 2012

'I'm not surprised. He hadn't looked out since the Feast of Stephen.'

RECIPE OF THE WEEK
Turkish Rice Pilaff with Chick Peas & Apricots
Serves 4

Prepare 10 mins **Cook** 25 mins
1 tbsp olive oil
1 essential Waitrose Medium Onion, finely sliced
2 garlic cloves, crushed
2 tsp ground cinnamon
2 tbsp essential Waitrose Tomato Purée
300g (11oz) basmati rice
600ml (1 pint) vegetable stock or water
400g can essential Waitrose Chick Peas, drained
100g (4oz) Wholesome Soft Apricots, snipped into pieces
2 tbsp flaked almonds
20g pack fresh coriander, chopped

1. Heat the oil in a flameproof casserole, add the onion and garlic and cook over a gentle heat for 3 minutes until soft and golden, stirring regularly. Stir in the cinnamon and tomato purée and cook for a minute. Stir in the rice until coated in the oil. Add the stock or cold water, season and bring to the boil. Cover and simmer gently for 12 minutes until all the liquid is absorbed.
2. Add the chick peas, apricots and almonds, re-cover and cook gently for a further 5 minutes until the rice is tender, then stir in the chopped coriander and serve.
Recipe and photograph from Waitrose. More than 5,000 recipes can be found at www.waitrose.com/recipes

THIS WEEK'S TOP TIP
How to stay calm at Christmas

HEALTH

If you're hosting the family, be realistic. Don't strive for perfection by doing it all yourself: delegate.

It really doesn't matter whether someone cuts the carrots in rounds or sticks. If there are outstanding 'issues' between family members, encourage them to sort things out before the big day. And keep festivities short: one of the main reasons why rows erupt is because everyone has been cooped up together for too long.

If things are getting heated, defuse the situation promptly – suggesting an afternoon walk is a good tactic.

ALL THINGS BRIGHT AND BEAUTIFUL
Holly
Holly berries are an essential part of Christmas decorations but they're also a vital food source for birds, especially blackbirds. The seed within the berry tends to pass through the bird's digestive tract unharmed, so it's a two-way deal: the bird gets fed and the holly seed gets dispersed. Traditional weather lore has it that when holly berries are bountiful, a hard winter will follow.

DON'T QUOTE ME, BUT...
'Turn your wounds into wisdom'
Oprah Winfrey

**DECEMBER
DRINK OF THE MONTH**

EGG NOG

Just the thing to
serve around the festive
fireside

*1 British Lion Marked egg
½ tsp pure vanilla extract
2 tbsp caster (superfine) sugar
125ml (4fl oz) cream
125ml (4fl oz) milk
Large pinch freshly grated nutmeg,
plus extra for sprinkling
3 large ice cubes*

Crack the egg into a heavy-duty
blender and add the vanilla, sugar,
cream, milk, nutmeg and ice cubes.
Blend until smooth and frothy. Pour
into a medium glass and sprinkle
with a little extra grated nutmeg.

BADGER'S BLOG

'I WOULD NO LONGER BE REFERRED TO AS A PET, BUT AS AN ANIMAL COMPANION'

Badger muses on her redefined role within the home –
and looks forward to Christmas

BOG recently
announced that
because of
something called 'political
correctness and animal
rights', I would no longer be
referred to as a pet, but as
an 'animal companion'.

Much as I approve of the
sentiment, it's completely
wrong. I am, in every
respect, an animal
custodian. It is my job to
protect my home and my
pack. Obviously I can't do
this all the time because
I need 14 hours' sleep
a day. But the rest of the
time nothing moves
without me knowing
about it. Especially if it's
a cat. GRRRRR.

But those filthy
furballs aren't the only
things I hate. Here's a list
of my other pet dislikes (or should
that be 'companion' dislikes?): combs,
scissors, baths, aloe vera dog
shampoo, vets, cats, squirrels, rats,
worm pills and vets (but I think I've
already mentioned the last).

Here's a list of things I love (in no
particular order): walks, sniffs, treats,
cheese that accidentally falls off the
kitchen table, chasing rabbits, dog
chews, bones, anything that humans
eat (except sprouts) and anything
that smells yuk (like fox poo). And
then there's my boyfriend Wilf,
obviously. And then there's Christmas.
I love Christmas. The DFLs always
bring a tree indoors for me, and put
lots of interesting things underneath
it in boxes. These need to be opened,
of course, so I provide a lot of help
in that respect. They don't hang

chocolate coins off the branches any
more after I ate them a few years ago.
BOG was very impressed that
I managed to get the foil wrappers off
and leave them in a pile. Naturally
I was sick shortly afterwards, which
meant that I didn't enjoy my
Christmas bone quite as much as
I usually do.

So that's another year nearly
finished. The home is in one piece, my
pack is safe, and we're all looking
forward to Christmas dinner. My work
is done. But if they come anywhere
near me with a Santa scarf... GRRRR.

Name this month: *Minky Mo Mos.*
Best moment: *Chased Hyacinth up
a tree. The window cleaner was away.
She was up there all Christmas Day.*

RECIPE OF THE WEEK
Savoy Cabbage Parcels with Mushrooms & Ricotta
Serves 4

Prepare 20 mins **Cook** 30 mins
1 medium essential Waitrose Savoy Cabbage
1 tsp olive oil
2 shallots, finely chopped
1 clove garlic, crushed
100g (4oz) chestnut mushrooms, chopped
1 tsp caraway seeds
½ x 250g tub essential Waitrose Italian Ricotta
50g (2oz) LOVE Life Pine Kernels, toasted
350g tub essential Waitrose Tomato and Basil Sauce
Crusty bread, to serve

1. Preheat the oven to 200C/400F/gas 6. Remove 8 outer leaves from the cabbage and shred the remainder, discarding any thick stalks. Cook the whole leaves in a large pan of boiling water for 2-3 minutes until tender. Drain and run under cold water, then pat dry with kitchen paper. Cut out the base of the central stalk on each leaf.
2. Heat the oil in a large non-stick frying pan and add the shallots, garlic and mushrooms. Cook for 3-4 minutes, stirring, until softened, then add the shredded cabbage, caraway seeds and a dash of water. Season and cover the pan. Cook over a gentle heat for 5 minutes until the cabbage is very tender. Stir in the ricotta and toasted pine kernels.
3. Spoon the sauce into the base of an ovenproof dish. Using a teaspoon, divide the mushroom mixture between the cabbage leaves and roll up into neat parcels, folding in the ends. Tuck into the dish so they fit neatly. Bake for 15-20 minutes until heated through. Serve with crusty bread.
Recipe and photograph from Waitrose. More than 5,000 recipes can be found at www.waitrose.com/recipes

THIS WEEK'S TOP TIP
Scrutinise your bank statement

MONEY
Whether you bank online or receive paper statements, take half an hour to go through your monthly outgoings with a fine toothcomb. Look closely at standing orders/direct debits. Many subscriptions are on a rolling renewal and you don't tend to be notified when they are about to renew – if you no longer use memberships to the max, cancel them. And watch out for recurring payments – unlike direct debits or standing orders these are harder to cancel, but it can be done – your bank should help.

ALL THINGS BRIGHT AND BEAUTIFUL
Old man's beard
The fluffy seedheads of old man's beard trail through hedges along footpaths and roadways. Its alternative name of traveller's joy was coined by John Gerard writing in the 16th century, as he enjoyed the sight of it 'adorning ways and hedges, where people travel'. It's a species of wild clematis, which means it has flexible stems ideal for twisting into wreaths for Christmas decorations.

DON'T QUOTE ME, BUT...

'Behind every great man is a woman rolling her eyes'

Jim Carrey

BRITISH BAND AID

Eel Pie hosted the good and the great of rock music

EEL PIE ISLAND
River Thames, Twickenham,
London
Size: 5 acres
Population: 120

When local antiques dealer Michael Snapper bought the **Eel Pie Hotel** in 1951, it's unlikely he could have dreamt what a seminal impact it would have on the British music scene. The roster of musicians who performed there includes a vast array of luminaries, many of whom were unknowns when they played their early gigs.

Snapper's hotel became a magnet for fans of jazz and skiffle, drawn to hear acts such as George Melly, Acker Bilk, The Temperance Seven, Lonnie Donegan and the late, great Ivor Cutler. In 1956 the Eelpiland Jazz Club issued its members with cards that resembled passports – a declaration, if one were needed, that Eel Pie was truly a place apart. Indeed, up until the following year, when the island's first-ever bridge linked it with the Twickenham bank of the Thames, the only way to get over to the island was by a punt hauled on a chain.

As the 1950s gave way to the 60s, so jazz and skiffle made way for music with a slightly harder edge. The island provided early audiences for Pink Floyd, Long John Baldry, ska and reggae star Jimmy Cliff, The Moody Blues, The Yardbirds and John Mayall's Bluesbreakers (featuring Eric Clapton). However, the band most associated with the island is The Rolling Stones, often playing to crowds so large they poured off the island and across the bridge.

Eel Pie Hotel was not a luxurious set-up. It revelled in its advanced state of decay and was a place where there were apparently no rules – a state of affairs that naturally attracted the youth of the day. Eventually, the police demanded the closure of the hotel – citing safety grounds – unless substantial repairs were made. Unable to meet the astronomical costs involved, on September 4, 1967 Snapper was forced to shut up shop.

In 1969 the music venue was reborn and another slew of bands with household names graced the stage, including The Who, Black Sabbath, Led Zeppelin, Deep Purple, Hawkwind and Genesis. By this time, the hotel had been thoroughly taken over by squatters and in the winter of 1970/71 the residents began pulling the hotel building apart to use as firewood. Four weeks after Snapper had made a planning application to replace the hotel with housing, it burnt down.

Today, some of the island's 57 varied properties occupy the site of the hotel. The best time to visit is on one of its occasional open studio days. If you're lucky you might bump into island resident Trevor Baylis, who invented his famous wind-up radio here.

HOW TO GET THERE
From Twickenham railway station it's less than half a mile through the town to the footbridge over to Eel Pie Island. For the full Eel Pie experience, go on one of the biannual open weekends (usually June and December), when you can visit the island's 26 artists' studios.

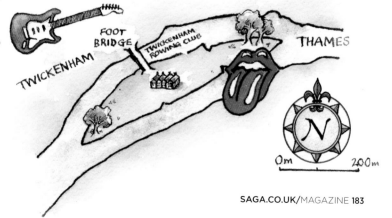

THIS WEEK'S TOP TIP
Fuller lips in an instant

BEAUTY

To boost thin lips, start by applying lipstick as normal, without taking it over the edge of the natural lip line.

Then use a lip pencil to pick up a small amount of lipstick from your lips and gently nudge it over the line – use a pencil in a matching shade and no one will be any the wiser. It's an effective and subtle solution that's infinitely better than drawing on a false mouth.

ALL THINGS BRIGHT AND BEAUTIFUL
Heron

Birdwatching is often simpler in winter when trees and bushes are bare. Herons become much easier to spot standing motionless in the shallows of a pond or lake when all the marginal vegetation has died back. They're a surprising sight silhouetted against the sky from the branches of a tree – it's not hard to imagine their prehistoric ancestors. On the ground they may stand with their neck outstretched or hunched; when flying they draw their heads back and let their legs trail – a useful pointer to help distinguish them from birds of prey in flight (herons have a 1.8m/6ft wingspan).

RECIPE OF THE WEEK
Roast Vegetable Medley with Stilton & Chestnuts
Serves 4

Prepare 20 mins **Cook** 1 hour 15 mins

3 tbsp Waitrose French Walnut Oil or olive oil
4 large parsnips, peeled and quartered lengthways
4 large red potatoes, peeled and cut lengthways into 6 wedges
4 large carrots, scrubbed and halved lengthways
2 large onions, cut into 6 wedges
200g pack Merchant Gourmet Cooked and Peeled Whole Chestnuts, roughly chopped
Juice of 1 lime
200g (7oz) Waitrose Rich and Creamy Blue Stilton, crumbled

1. Preheat the oven to 200C/400F/gas 6. Add 2 tbsp of the oil to a large roasting tin and place in the oven for 5 minutes.
2. Mix all the prepared vegetables in the hot oil and roast for 1 hour, turning occasionally, until tender and golden brown. Mix in the chopped chestnuts and continue to cook for a further 10 minutes.
3. Mix together the lime juice, the remaining olive oil and a little seasoning. Divide the vegetables between serving bowls, scatter the cheese on top and drizzle with the lime dressing. Serve warm with crusty bread.
Recipe and photograph from Waitrose. More than 5,000 recipes can be found at www.waitrose.com/recipes

DON'T QUOTE ME, BUT...

'Middle age is when your broad mind and narrow waist begin to change places'

E. Joseph Cossman

More languages – at least 300 – are spoken in London than in any other city in the world

If a whale is beached on the British coast, the Queen can claim the tail. If we had a king on the throne, he could claim the head

At any given time 7% of the world's population is drunk

Bigfoot mystery explained.

WOTEVA!
Teenage translator

Cellfish
Someone who talks on their mobile phone when it is rude to do so

Farting terms
That point in a relationship where both parties feel so comfortable in each other's company that they are happy to break wind together. Aw, who says that romance is dead?

Premature exasperation
Getting annoyed about something before hearing the full facts

UNEXPECTED ANNIVERSARIES
MIND THE GAP!
December 2014 is the 62nd anniversary of: a double-decker bus jumping the space between the two halves of Tower Bridge

One day in December 1952, Albert Gunton was unlucky enough to be driving his number 78 double-decker bus across Tower Bridge when it started to rise.

He realised that he wouldn't be able to stop in time to avoid going into the water and, making a split-second decision, decided he would go for it. He accelerated and jumped the three-foot gap, landing on the north bascule (bascule is French for see-saw), which had not started to rise. None of his dozen passengers was seriously hurt, and he received £10 for his bravery. He also appeared later on the TV show *What's My Line?*

FROM 'ONE MAKE CHRISTMAS' & FESTIVE DECORATIONS BY ROS BADGER WITH ELSPETH THOMPSON, PHOTOGRAPH BENJAMIN J MURPHY. PUBLISHED BY HARPERCOLLINS. @ROSBADGER

PET OF THE MONTH
Pieces of eight!

Name: Crowky
Owner's name: Jayne Blackadder
Best habit: Wolf-whistling while sitting on your shoulder
Worst habit: Wiping beak on curtains
Likes: Anything he shouldn't have
Dislikes: Vacuum cleaner noise; he dunks his head in the water bowl
Personality: Confused
Naughtiest moment: Dive-bombing people when they are eating
Most human trait: Loves a bath, then a blow-dry from the hairdryer

---

TOP TECHIE TIP
The tweetest feeling

For the uninitiated, Twitter is a means of sharing your thoughts via computer or mobile. Users post messages – called tweets – using no more than 140 characters, including spaces. But why? If Facebook is a way of communicating with friends, Twitter is like stepping onto a stage to address an audience – albeit very briefly.

Twitter is great for homing in on people who share a cause or interest, and for swapping ideas. One tweet can replace an email to dozens of people. To set up an account, go to www.twitter.com, choose a username and password, and start tweeting.

JOKE OF THE MONTH
A man walks into a doctor's surgery with a stick of celery in one ear, a carrot in the other and a grape up his nose. Confused, the man asks: 'Doctor, what's wrong with me?' The doctor looks at the man and replies: 'You're not eating properly!'

sent in by Barbara Tanner

HOW TO MAKE CRANBERRY CHRISTMAS DECORATIONS

Cranberries have a rich wine colour and lovely plump shape – they're a wonderful alternative to shop-bought decorations. Traditionally they symbolise peace and the earth's abundance

YOU WILL NEED
Cranberries
Darning needle
String and/or florists' wire

CRANBERRY HEARTS, CIRCLES AND STARS
1. Use florists' wire, or a malleable alternative that will hold its shape, to thread together a short length of cranberries.
2. Twist the two ends of wire together and shape into a heart, circle, star or any other festive shape that takes your fancy.
3. Attach a length of ribbon or string and hang your decoration on the tree, on door handles or on the wall during the Christmas season.

CRANBERRY GARLAND
1. The simplest way to use cranberries as a decoration is to thread them onto thin twine or coloured string using a darning needle.

2. Thread the needle with twine and tie a large knot at one end, then begin threading the fruit, pushing the needle through the fruit from side to side, rather than top to bottom.
3. When your garland is long enough, tie another knot to finish.

TIPS
Cranberry decorations will keep for year after year, but remember that the berries will shrink as they dry and you will need to tighten them slightly on the wire or twine. The berries on freshly made decorations are unlikely to be completely dry by Twelfth Night, so leave them for a few days in a warm space such as an airing cupboard, then carefully pull the string or wire through the dry fruit to make the garland more compact.

You could also use the wire method to make a small wreath to hang on the front door. The berries will last longer outside, but note that if they freeze they will disintegrate as they thaw, so bring the wreath inside on freezing nights if possible.

If you have any cranberries left, place some in the base of a jam jar and stand a white candle among them for a table decoration.

USE IT OR LOSE IT
BRAIN EXERCISE
Give your grey matter a work-out

SUDOKU
The game of logic. Place each of the digits 1 to 9 in each row, column and 3x3 box. There is only one solution.

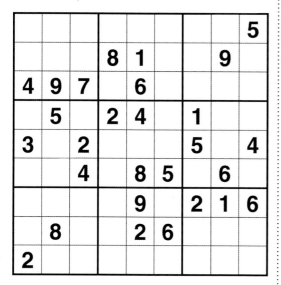

GRAMMAR CHALLENGE CHRISTMAS SPECIAL
The Lynne Truss test This month there are some serious ambiguities to be ironed out, too. See below for the corrected version.

from the cable car capped with snow and surounded by mist me and my fellow travellers viewed the awesome mountains putting on hats and sunglasses to cope with the fierce winter sun descending from the terminal to ground level we saw mountain goats which had left tracks in the snow before visiting the bar for a first taste of alpine hospitality the guide explained the fir trees which stood in serried ranks up the mountainside formed a vital anchor helping prevent avalanches in the winter and the inevitable landslides which came in the summer

DECEMBER'S GENERAL KNOWLEDGE QUIZ
1 In *A Christmas Carol*, what are the first names of Bob Cratchit's eldest daughters?
A. Sally and Molly, B. Martha and Belinda, C. Constance and Melody, D. Tiff and Tilly

2 In which city will you find Wenceslas Square?
A. Prague, B. Budapest, C. Sarajevo, D. Bratislava

3 In the Australian Christmas novelty song *Six White Boomers*, what are 'boomers'?
A. Large parakeets, B. Albino koalas, C. Adult kangaroos, D. Glasses of frothy-headed beer

4 Who recorded a duet of *The Little Drummer Boy* with Bing Crosby?
A. David Bowie, B. Bono, C. Jon Bon Jovi, D. Paul McCartney

5 In which country did the Decembrist revolt, led by disaffected army officers, take place in 1825?
A. Poland, B. Russia, C. Spain, D. Mexico

6 Who gave Channel 4's first *Alternative Christmas Message* in 1993?
A. Dame Edna Everage, B. Quentin Crisp, C. Johnny Rotten, D. George Galloway

7 In which country is Boxing Day not an official holiday?
A. USA, B. Canada, C. Ireland, D. New Zealand

8 Future Prime Minister Edward Heath won the 1969 Sydney to Hobart yacht race. What was the name of his boat?
A. Blue Dawn, B. Azure II, C. Morning Cloud, D. Clear Majority

9 Who directed the 1993 film *The Nightmare Before Christmas*?
A. Wes Craven, B. John Carpenter, C. Tim Burton, D. Abel Ferrara

10 What did the BBC broadcast for the first time in 1923?
A. An aeroplane taking off from Croydon airport,
B. *A Letter from America*,
C. The New Year's Eve crowds at Trafalgar Square,
D. The chimes of Big Ben

From the cable car, my fellow travellers and I viewed the awesome, snow-capped mountains, which were surrounded by mist. We put on hats and sunglasses to cope with the fierce winter sun before descending to ground level and visiting a bar for our first taste of alpine hospitality. We saw tracks left in the snow by mountain goats and the guide explained that the fir trees that stood in serried ranks up the mountainside formed a vital anchor, helping to prevent avalanches in the winter and the inevitable landslides that come in the summer.

ANSWERS
1. B, **2.** A,
3. C, **4.** A,
5. B, **6.** B,
7. A, **8.** C,
9. C, **10.** D

8	4	9	1	5	7	6	3	2
3	5	7	6	2	4	9	8	1
6	1	2	8	9	3	5	4	7
7	9	3	5	8	1	4	7	9
4	8	5	9	6	2	7	1	3
9	7	1	3	4	2	8	5	6
1	3	8	2	9	5	7	6	4
7	9	6	4	1	8	3	2	5
5	2	4	7	3	6	1	9	8

Your chance to win one of
10
subscriptions to
Saga MAGAZINE

Please send
your name, address,
telephone number
and email address, if you
have one, to:

Saga Magazine
Giveaway
FREEPOST CU250
Folkestone
Kent
CT20 1BR

Closing date: January 31, 2014
The subscription is for one year
(12 issues).

For full terms and conditions, go to:
www.saga.co.uk/magazinegiveaway

**12 issues
for just
£19.95**

**Liked this Yearbook?
Why not try some of the other
products Saga has to offer.**

Subscribe today!

If you've enjoyed reading this, why not subscribe to Saga Magazine, or give it as a gift subscription?

Take out a subscription and enjoy:

- 12 issues of the UK's bestselling monthly magazine for just £19.95
- Exclusive discounts on books, holidays, hotel breaks and more
- Reader-only events such as theatre trips and outdoor concerts
- A full money-back guarantee on all unmailed issues if you are not happy
- FREE delivery direct to your door

To subscribe, simply:

☎ Call FREEPHONE **0800 056 1057** (lines are open Mon-Fri, 9am-5pm)

🖰 Go online at **www.saga.co.uk/subs** and enter ANN13

Please note, this offer is for UK subscriptions only.

Saga does a lot more than produce a bestselling magazine. Sixty years of experience has made us the leading provider of all kinds of things for the over-50s: fabulous holidays, award-winning insurance and personal finance products – and much more. **See the full range of Saga services at saga.co.uk**

Pedigree Books, Beech Hill House, Walnut Gardens, Exeter EX4 4DH